Fabulous Fashion

1907-67

from The Costume Institute
The Metropolitan Museum of Art, New York

Sponsored by The Australian Women's Weekly and the Sussan Corporation (Aust.) Limited

Arranged by the International Cultural Corporation of Australia Limited

VENUES:
National Gallery of Victoria
Art Gallery of New South Wales

Catalogue written by

Stella Blum and Louise Hamer
The Costume Institute
The Metropolitan Museum of Art, New York

Edited by Rowena Clark

Copyright: International Cultural Corporation
of Australia Limited

ISBN 0 9594122 1 2

Colour Photography: Joshua Greene
Typesetting: All Graphic Industries, Aust.
Color Separations: Show-Ads Colour Centre, Aust.
Printed by: Wilke and Company Limited
37-49 Browns Road, Clayton, Victoria.

Front Cover: Evening Wrap by Paquin – French 1912

FOREWORD

We are proud and pleased to present this superb collection of costumes and accessories from The Costume Institute of The Metropolitan Museum of Art in New York.

This Exhibition, managed by the International Cultural Corporation of Australia Limited, is unique in the history of major exhibitions in Australia. It presents fashion and costume as an expressive art form which mirrors the social changes of the periods represented.

It provides us with a unique opportunity to view the brilliant creations of such masters of fashion as Worth, Poiret, Chanel, Fortuny and Schiaparelli, whose designs reflect the enormous developments of our century.

We are most grateful to the Director and staff of The Metropolitan Museum of Art and especially Mrs Stella Blum, Curator, and the staff of The Costume Institute for making this Exhibition possible.

We would like to thank the Visual Arts Board of the Australia Council and the Department of Home Affairs for their cooperation and assistance in arranging Australian Government indemnity for the Australian tour.

The Directors and staffs of the participating galleries have given most generously of their time and expertise in the preparation of this Exhibition, which is only one of the many on-going programmes of those galleries.

This magnificent display has been made possible by the most generous sponsorship of Sussan Corporation (Aust.) Ltd. and the Australian Women's Weekly. We are very grateful to them.

We deeply appreciate the combination of Government and private sector resources which has provided both financial support and the talents of an extraordinary range of people to assist this complex project. It should be an inspiration for future sponsors of the arts in this country.

James Leslie
Chairman

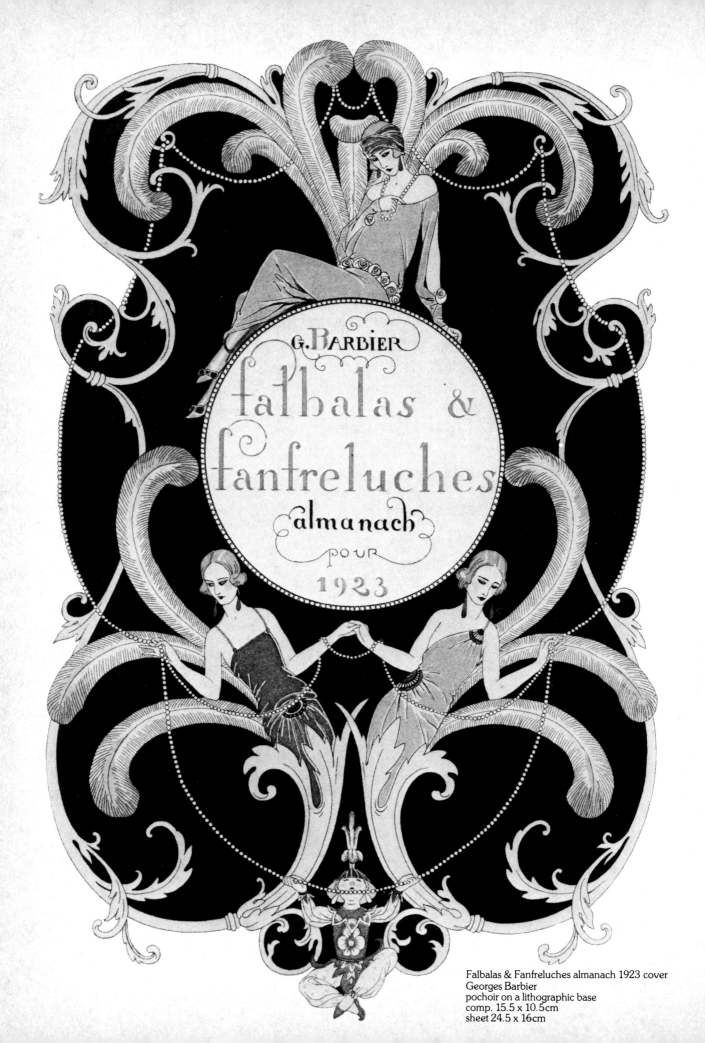

Falbalas & Fanfreluches almanach 1923 cover
Georges Barbier
pochoir on a lithographic base
comp. 15.5 x 10.5cm
sheet 24.5 x 16cm

The historical and artistic evolution of costume stands as a special and particularly important field of study, for it is at once the most personal and precise reflection of the individual and collective taste of any period in a society, as well as an index to general statements on the social customs and aesthetics of that time. Though fashion remains in a constant state of flux, costumes survive as records of predominant styles at any given moment. Costumes provide a barometric reading of the changes in style, and for this reason alone their presence is invaluable.

The Costume Institute, founded in 1937 by Irene Lewisohn, moved to The Metropolitan Museum of Art in 1946, a new association that emphasized costume design as a true form of art. The focus of the Institute has consistently been to collect the most splendid and beautiful examples of the art of dress – those costumes that also admirably reflect the artistic styles of their respective periods.

The Costume Institute has a strong and extensive collection and has played an active role in mounting exhibitions that have travelled both in the United States and abroad. We are particularly delighted to have had the occasion to create a new exhibition for our colleagues in Australia, and we look forward to future collaborative ventures. I would like to thank Stella Blum, Curator of the Costume Institute, for making possible this major loan exhibition.

Philippe de Montebello
Director
The Metropolitan Museum of Art

Dœuillet

WORTH

Gazette du Bon Ton, issue no. 3, 1920,
p.1. 19 No title
Mario Simon
lithography
comp. 24½ x 19cm
sheet 24½ x 19cm

Over the past decade the National Gallery of Victoria has been the venue for a number of comprehensive exhibitions of costumes and accessories. The most notable of these, 'Lady of Fashion' 1800-1935, was mounted in 1975 and featured some one hundred and fifty 19th and 20th century costumes which had been acquired from the Anne Schofield collection with a subsidy from the State Government. Such exhibitions have engendered a growing awareness within the community of costume as a vital element in our heritage, and as a poignant reflection of the artistic style and social customs of a period. This newly awakened interest has led to the consolidation of the National Gallery's permanent collection in the Southern Hemisphere.

However, with 'Fabulous Fashion 1907-1967 , we are witnessing for the first time in this country, a major travelling exhibition comprising material drawn from one of the world's greatest art museums and focussing on the highly fluid art of costume. To be more specific, the exhibition traces the development of artistic style as it applies to dress design in the years between 1907 and 1967. It identifies the contribution to this period of remarkable stylistic evolution of such influential designers as Paul Poiret, 'Coco' Chanel, Balenciaga and Yves Saint Laurent. The exhibition evokes the creative intuition of these designers whose exclusive works expressed the aspirations and spirit of their age and proclaimed the social status of their clients.

The selection of costumes for 'Fabulous Fashion' was undertaken by Stella Blum, Curator of the Costume Institute of the Metropolitan Museum of Art in New York. We wish to acknowledge the great energy and expertise which she and her colleagues have contributed to the exhibition and the preparation of this catalogue.

Rowena Clark

Rowena Clark
Assistant Curator of Costumes and Textiles.
The National Gallery of Victoria.

FASHIONS 1907-67

Stella Blum

Chanel once said that nothing is fashion until it is seen on the streets. This, of course, is true – indeed. Fashion is a kind of social contract, tacit agreement about what constitutes hypothetical perfection regarding dress and appearance. Evolutionary in nature, like the society that supports it, fashion tries to keep pace with shifting social climates and to evolve ideals that will best conform to the changes that ensue. Inspiration for new fashions does not spring from thin air. In fashion, just as in all creative endeavours, valid statements are first the products of talented people sensitive to the world around them, who also have the ability to give tangible substance to ideas and values.

From the turn of the century until the second half of the 1960s, most new fashion concepts generated from the French *haute couture*. Catering to a privileged few and keeping just the right distance ahead of the familiar, *couturiers* in Paris designed creations that enhanced their clients and pronounced their superior status. These clients in turn, became figures of admiration, and thus set a pattern for others to imitate.

The sixty-year period from 1907 to 1967 was one of monumental changes. One need only compare the costumes of 1907 to those of 1967 to realize how much evolution must have occurred to produce such vast differences.

1907-08: In the opening years of the 20th century, women's fashions were in the terminal phase of the 1890s styles. Although Victorianism had given way to Edwardianism and there was some loosening of morals, women continued to encase themselves in tightly-laced corsets, while masses of ruffles at the hem restricted the easy mobility of their legs. The fashionable silhouette was the serpentine S-shape, with the chest extended forward in a formidable mono-bosom, linked in the middle by an incredibly small waist to full, rounded hips.

For day, women wore gowns or blouses with high, stiff collars to give their necks a swan-like elegance. In the evening, rosy plump shoulders grew out of low *decolletages*. Made of pale, soft fabrics – mainly silk – gowns were trimmed with a profusion of braids, laces, and all manner of confections. The pompadour hair style expanded in volume, and huge oversized hats were designed to accommodate them. The keyword was womanliness. Fashionable women kept their circle small and elite. Their lives were slow-paced and concentrated on the good life. It was the *belle époque*. The designer, Jacques Doucet, in whose *atelier* both Paul Poiret and Madeleine Vionnet had been apprenticed, understood the mood of this era and created some of the finest and most elegant fashions for his wealthy and stylish clients. Other superb designs came from the House of Worth, which had opened in 1858 and rode at the peak of its popularity until World War I.

1909-13: When Edward VII died in 1909, the fashions dominant at the beginning of his reign were already in eclipse. By then, Paris had begun to resound with and react to fresh sounds in music and new forms in art, literature, and theatre. In 1909 the *Ballets Russes* made their first astonishing appearance in Paris. Produced by Serge Diaghilev, and designed by such artists as Leon Bakst and Alexandre Benois, the *Ballets Russes* were stunning spectacles. The radiantly vibrant colours of the sets and the dancers in exotic costumes worn over uncorseted supple bodies evoked heady Oriental fantasies that made the current fashions look dull, faded, and dated. The fashion world was ready for a change, and the *Ballets Russes* provided exciting alternatives. Costumes became ablaze with colour and bold accents. Several years earlier the designer, Paul Poiret, had proposed gowns that fell loosely from the bosom in a classical manner and could be worn without corsets. This silhouette now received popular sanction. However, although the torso was released, freedom was still limited. Constriction was transferred from the waist to the ankles. The hems of skirts became so narrow that they caused women to take tiny, mincing steps – hence the term 'hobble skirt'. The popularity of the Argentinian tango just before World War I freed women's legs from their fashionable shackles. To accommodate the steps of this dance, skirts were discreetly split or lapped over in front. For the first time in centuries, if only on occasion, the woman's leg above the ankle was exposed to public gaze. Nevertheless, women's fashion remained essentially feminine. Gowns conformed to or accented female curves, turning women into temptresses or 'vampires'.

1914-19: The scene changed after 1914 during World War I, when, due to a manpower shortage, women were drawn into the labour force to help with the war effort. Because their new occupations required more functional apparel, they began to wear clothes that had a simpler, more masculine appearance. Wartime involved them in activities previously in the domain of men, giving them a taste of new freedoms. Having experienced a modicum of emancipation, women were determined to hold the liberty they had gained, even after the war was over.

1920-28: By the 1920s, women sought in force, to find equality with men. In their efforts to emulate them they cut their hair into the boyish bob and defeminized their figures by flattening their bosoms and hips. By 1925 women's legs were exposed to the knees, releasing them for mobility and action. The aesthetics in fashion reflected the hard-edged elements begun in the arts. Abstract and geometric in design, clothes depended on the movement of living women to lend shape and sexuality to forms that otherwise would appear sterile. This style was totally in step with the pulsating dynamism of an era seeking to erode the restrictive social, political, economic, and moral concepts left over from the previous century. The focus was on youth, movement, and speed. Liberated bodies sought excitement in round-the-clock dancing of the Charleston, the Fox Trot, and the Black Bottom. To augment the new rhythms, the gowns of the twenties – basically unshaped rectangles – were embellished with beading, fringes, ruffles, and all manner of embroidery designed to accent each motion of the body.

1929-39: By 1929 Western society found itself spent and confused. Its world was rocked by the collapse of the American economy. The tempo slackened and gave in to a kind of languor. Insulating themselves against unpleasant realities, the wealthy spun a radiant cocoon around their own universe. Turning their backs on the hardships of others, they created for themselves a life of international luxury. Fashion dictated a season in Paris or other European capitals, the Riviera in the summer, and St Moritz in the winter. Pleasure was sought rather than thrills, suavity dulled the edges of rudeness, and idleness replaced the pursuit of speed. For them, time appeared to stand still. Fashion naturally reflected this new development.

Hemlines dropped. By 1930 they dropped to below calf-length for day, and in the evening they touched the ground. Devoid of trimmings, gowns fitted like second skins, smooth, slinky, and backless for evening. There was little need for movement. Mere breathing would incur sensuality. Lounging pyjamas were worn for leisure hours, and bathing suits, more for basking in the sun than for swimming, were designed to flatter and reveal.

By the mid-1930s there was a growing awareness that war was imminent. As though to thwart an impending catastrophe, people sought solace in nostalgia, romance, and festive peasant costumes. Dance music alternated between the sweet, sentimental, dreamy sounds of 'swing' and the scintillating Latin American rhythms of the samba, rhumba, and conga. In fashion, a strange duality occurred. While evening clothes tended towards feminine frivolity, for day, man-tailored suits returned. To accent maleness, shoulders were squared off and padded into exaggerated widths. Tiny, whimsically-trimmed hats and costume jewellery, along with artificial flowers, added a touch of gaiety to the general sombreness of the costumes.

The beginning of World War II in 1939 was the end of an era. For over three decades Paris had led the world in cultural activities. Musicians, writers, artists, and designers all converged there, creating a fertile climate that would spawn and nurture new expressions in every artistic field. Paris gave birth to Cubism, Fauvism, Surrealism, Futurism, and Art Deco. Igor Stravinsky, Claude Debussy, Erik Satie, Maurice Ravel, the blues, and the Dixieland band, introduced sounds that were fresh, vital, and exhilarating. Such writers as Guillaume Apollinaire, André Gide, James Joyce, F. Scott Fitzgerald, and Ernest Hemingway, produced works that altered the course of literature. Fashion designers, very much a part of this artistic circle, responded to its stimuli and devised clothes in step with these rapidly changing times.

Paul Poiret, through his unique flair for the fantastic, enticed women into wearing clothes that were less restrictive, paving the way towards the unconstrained fashions of the 1920s. Jeanne Hallée and the Callot Soeurs gave their designs a patina of elegance and luxury. With her hip-extending *robe de style* gowns, Jeanne Lanvin lent variety to the standard tubular form of the twenties. The coming popularity of sportswear was envisioned by the firm of Hermès. An Englishman, Captain Edward Molyneux, and an American, Main Rousseau Bocher (Mainbocher), infused a refined touch of class into the clothes they designed. Madeleine Vionnet introduced the use of bias, a new concept of clothing construction, designing gowns of classical beauty. Elsa Schiaparelli added a flavour of theatre and a measure of gaiety to fashions during the doleful period just before World War II. Coco Chanel brought the 20th century to fashions. In their functional simplicity, her designs are as appropriate today as when she first devised them.

1940-45: When Paris fell in 1940, the fashion world had to look to other sources for direction. Americans turned to their own designers. By this time, there was a great deal of designing done in America, especially in New York, but much of it was a version of what had been proposed in Paris. Wealthy and fashionable ladies, when not dressed in the French *couture,* wore clothes either made by private dressmakers or custom-made by such expensive establishments as Bergdorf-Goodman, Eldridge, Manning, and H. Jaeckel and Sons. The names of American designers were seldom made known, and labels generally carried only the name of manufacturers or stores that sold them.
After America entered the war in 1941, department stores and fashion magazines in a spirit of patriotism began to give American designers the same recognition previously reserved for the French *couturiers.* Gradually, Norman Norell, Charles James, Philip Mangone and others, became known for their elegant sumptuous clothes. Adrian, famous for the ultimate glamour of his designs for film-stars, opened a *couture* and ready-to-wear salon in 1942.
The war years, 1941-45 were grim. The gruesome realities of war, the loss of loved ones, shortages, and regulations made a focus on fashion appear superficial. Yet, although styles

seemed to change very little, the events of this period were eventually to revolutionize the concept of fashion. Accepting current conditions, such American designers as Claire McCardell and Vera Maxwell set about to interject quality and design into less lofty social levels, more suited to the lifestyle of America's vast middle class. While this new view of fashion grew out of the exigencies of wartime, it continued in America after the armistice. For a time it ran side-by-side with couture fashions, then gradually led to the democratization of fashion throughout the world. The most graphic example of this evolvement is the unprecedented phenomenon of blue jeans.

1946-53: After a short spell devoted to reconstruction and a reorientation to peace, in April 1947 Christian Dior launched his 'New Look'. His timing was so perfect that practically overnight the new silhouette became a sensational success. Somehow, he had intuitively reached back to the mid-19th century for his inspiration, to a period that the costume historian, C. W. Cunnington, called the era of 'The Perfect Lady'. The sloping shoulder, rounded bosom, nipped-in waist, and expanded hips, spelled female in capital letters. Due to a psychological reaction to wartime privations, its impact was so strong that within a year even secretaries and housewives were willing to suffer the discomfort of waistcinchers, the constriction of layers of petticoats, and the pain of walking in pointed shoes with high stiletto heels! There was a return to dressing-up for lunches, parties, and balls. For these occasions the *couture* designers, using magnificent fabrics richly decorated with beading, embroidery, laces, and braids, created clothes that rivalled in opulence those made at the turn of the century by Worth, Paquin, Beer and Doucet. Dior designed suits, dresses, and spectacular ballgowns that were so completely structured that the wearer was merely an armature to support them. Marcelle Chaumont carried on the classical tradition of Madeleine Vionnet. Mme Alix, who before the war had begun to design beautiful sculptural clothes as well as some with exotic overtones, returned to create in the same vein under her married name, Mme Grès. Cristobal Balenciaga not only produced suits that reflected his skill as a master tailor, but also ballgowns that drew superb forms from the aerodynamics of movement. Schiaparelli, having enjoyed great popularity before the war, tried to revive her salon. Her brief success was due chiefly to the talents of a young designer, Hubert Givenchy, who soon became famous in his own right. Other designers, such as Pierre Balmain, Jacques Fath, and Jacques Griffe, though perhaps less innovative, also created clothes that were beautiful representations of their period. Charles James, Norman Norell, and Arnold Scaasi, upheld *haute couture* standards in America.

1954-63: While this mood in fashion fed the post-war appetite for some of the luxuries of the 'good old days', it grew essentially out of a nostalgia to which time had lent glamour and a measure of security. In reality it was impractical and radically out of step with the social, economic, and technological changes that had emerged as a result of the war. In 1954, using the fashion acumen that was her genius, Chanel reopened her salon and startled the fashion world by reissuing the simple, functional designs that were her concept of what 20th century dressing should be. After the initial shock and some resistance, the logic of her statement caught on and, at least in the area of daywear, other designers soon followed suit. Even Dior agreed, and came out with his uncinched and unpadded H-line in 1954, and then with the A-line in 1955. Balenciaga, who had prophetically but unsuccessfully proposed an unfitted look in 1952, found his chemise and sack-back styles now not only accepted but also extensively copied. In 1957 Yves Saint Laurent introduced his famous 'trapeze' silhouette.
Yet, while women readily acknowledged the practicality of less restricting day clothes, they were reluctant to abandon the trussed-up discomfort of the New Look silhouette for evening. The short evening gown was the only concession to which they would accede.
A kind of euphoria settled in during the 1950s and persisted, at least on the surface, into the early 1960s. Romance had returned, and a record low unemployment rate brought with it unprecedented affluence. Technology provided not only labour-saving devices, but also ways to spend the hours released by these devices. For a while life took on the utopian aspect of a scene from *Camelot*. However, like the musical, it was based on fantasy.

1964-67: Three events occurred in 1964 that helped to launch a new era in fashion: the appearance of Mary Quant's mini-skirt on the international scene; the introduction of André Courrèges' 'space' clothes; and the arrival of the Beatles in New York. All found a receptive audience.
The children of the post-war 'baby-boom' were approaching their teens. By 1960 one-half of America's population was under twenty-five. England, France, and other European countries, also reported a sizeable increase in the proportion of young people.
Raised in a financially secure atmosphere by parents that had become increasingly permissive, youngsters began to assert themselves at an early age. Most mothers no longer chose clothes for their offspring. Such decisions were made by the children themselves, for whom peer pressure was more important than parental guidance. Formidable in number, and allowed to select and buy their own clothes, young people were able to tilt the focus of fashion in their direction. Designers began to cater to their age level and taste. By 1967 the ideal fashion look was that of a 'nymphet', a budding but underdeveloped young lady, as epitomized by the high-fashion model, Twiggy. In addition to Mary Quant and Courrèges, other designers, such as Pierre Cardin and Paco Rabanne, joined the roster of familiar fashion names. Their use of plastics, synthetics, and metals underscored the role of technological developments that were an outgrowth of the war, and went on to interact with the life-styles that followed. The fashion market became so youth-oriented that mature women, even at the risk of looking ridiculous, felt compelled to dress in a manner more suited to girls years their junior. The few hold-outs included women wealthy enough to turn to Saint Laurent, James, Galanos, Norell, or other *couture* designers who continued to create some clothes in classically timeless styles.
Confused and disillusioned by the past and awed by what the future might hold, the new generation picked up the undercurrents of disenchantment that had been fomenting since the late 1950s. In the late 1960s dissatisfaction with existing mores and values erupted into rebellion. Out of this would come a period of anti-fashion, a totally new attitude toward dressing that in due time would shape the fashions of today.

Stella Blum
Curator,
The Costume Institute

INDEX OF DESIGNERS

LÉPÉE, MARTIAL
During the early 20th century, Lépée was one of the lesser known of establishments who were to make a strong contribution to the art of fine tailoring.
Page 26.

MAINBOCHER
(1890-1976)
Formally a fashion artist and fashion editor of French *Vogue*, Mainbocher established his own house in Paris during 1929. He created elegant moulded sheath dresses with intricate cutting technique.
Page 48, 54.

MANGONE, PHILIP
Philip Mangone began his tailoring career in New York and later in Paris. At 27 he was master of his art and controlled his own business, fashioning superb coats and suits.
Page 64.

MANNING, ELDRIDGE
During the 1920s the New York designer, Eldridge Manning, created his romantic *robes de style* which echoed the styles of Jeanne Lanvin.
Page 40.

MAXWELL, VERA
(b. 1904)
Vera Maxwell was trained in sportswear and tailoring. She is a highly original and skilled designer who gained success with her classic mix-and-match separates.
Page 92.

McCARDELL, CLAIRE
(1906-58)
One of America's great innovators of fashion throughout the 1940s and 1950, Claire McCardell created easy-fitting clothes, which included the diaper bathing suit and the popover dress.
Page 88, 90.

MOLYNEUX, CAPTAIN EDWARD
(1891-1974)
Edward Molyneux moved to Paris and opened his own house in 1919. He was an important *couturier,* whose clothes were of timeless quality. The stage clothes he designed for Gertrude Lawrence became a legend.
Page 38, 42, 46.

NORELL, NORMAN
(1900-72)
Norman Norell is regarded as one of America's top designers. He is well known for his precision tailoring and used this to improve the quality of ready-to-wear clothing.
Page 84, 102.

PAQUIN
The house of Paquin was founded in 1891 by Madame Paquin. Her splendid designs were of exceptionally high quality. As a skilled organizer she became the only woman ever to be elected President of the Chambre Syndicale de la Couture Française.
Page 22.

POIRET, PAUL
(1879-1944)
Poiret established his own business during 1904 and was a designer of exceptional ability. He created garments of simplicity and elegance in vivid colours using oriental influences.
Page 24, 32, 34.

QUANT, MARY
(b. 1934)
Mary Quant is a British designer who opened the shop in Chelsea called 'Bazaar' during the mid-1950s. Her unconventional clothes started a whole new 'Chelsea' and 'Mod' look.
Page 94.

RABANNE, PACO
(b. 1934)
Paco Rabanne, a Spaniard working in Paris, caused a sensation in 1966 when he launched his collection of metal-linked plastic disc dresses; it was another triumph for the youth cult.
Page 96.

SAINT LAURENT, YVES
(b. 1936)
During 1957, Dior died, leaving the top design post to his assistant, Yves Saint Laurent. He was to launch the 'trapeze' line, and later, for his own house, the pea jacket, Mondrian-inspired dress, and the 'nude' look of 1966.
Page 68, 94.

SCAASI, ARNOLD
(b. 1931)
In 1956 Arnold Scaasi opened his own wholesale business, and in 1963 a custom salon. His creations in rich fabrics, are dramatic and glamorous.
Page 82.

SCHIAPARELLI, ELSA
(1890-1973)
Schiaparelli opened her first boutique in 1935. Her accessories, gowns and matching jackets, with their exaggerated shoulders and unusual decorations, became the rage in Paris.
Page 56, 58, 72, 88, 102, 104.

VIONNET, MADELEINE
(1876-1975)
On reopening her own house in 1918, Madeleine Vionnet successfully created her bias cut, using the finest velvets, crêpe de Chines and satins, to achieve the classic look of her clothes.
Page 50, 54, 56.

WORTH, CHARLES FREDERICK
(1826-95)
A dressmaker of exceptional flair and skill, Worth became a master in the art of *haute couture,* creating extravagant gowns for the Empress Eugenie and her entourage.
Page 18.

WORTH, JEAN PHILIPPE
(1856-?)
Jean Philippe Worth acquired professional training in art, from Camille Corot, and learned the skills of designing from his father. After the death of his father, Jean and his brother, Gaston, continued the House of Worth.
Page 18.

1. VISITING DRESS

Pale grey-green wool broadcloth, trimmed with white
machine lace and silver metallic embroidered net.
French, Circa 1907
Label: Doucet, Paris
Gift of Irma A. Bloomingdale, 1976.390.8

2. LATE AFTERNOON GOWN

Grey silk chiffon trimmed with dark grey velvet,
lace, soutache braid and chain stitch embroidery.
French, Circa 1907
Label: Beer, 7 Place Vendôme, Paris
Gift of Mrs. George Kent, CI 45.36.4

DOUCET, JACQUES (1860-1932)

Jacques Doucet was a Parisian, the son of Edouard Doucet
whose shop on the Rue de la Paix dealt in fine laces, bonnets
and gentlemen's shirts and cravats. Jacques showed a
profound and early interest in fashion. After the Franco-
Prussian war in 1871, he opened a department within his
father's business and started designing ladies' dresses.
Doucet's love and wide knowledge of French 18th-century art
brought a strong Rococo influence to his clothes with plentiful
laces, ribbons, panniers and flounces. This interest also led
him to acquire a magnificent collection of furniture and
paintings from the period with which he formed an art and
archeological library in Paris. Doucet exhibited at the Paris
Exposition of 1900 with Paquin and Worth. He apprenticed
both Poiret and Vionnet during his career. When he retired in
1928, he merged his house with the lesser-known Doeuillet.

BEER

Beer was the first *couturier* to open a house on the historic
Place Vendôme in Paris, about 1905. A maker of fine lingerie
as well as dresses, his label was a status symbol for many
women. 'Conservative elegance for conservative patrons'
was his rule.

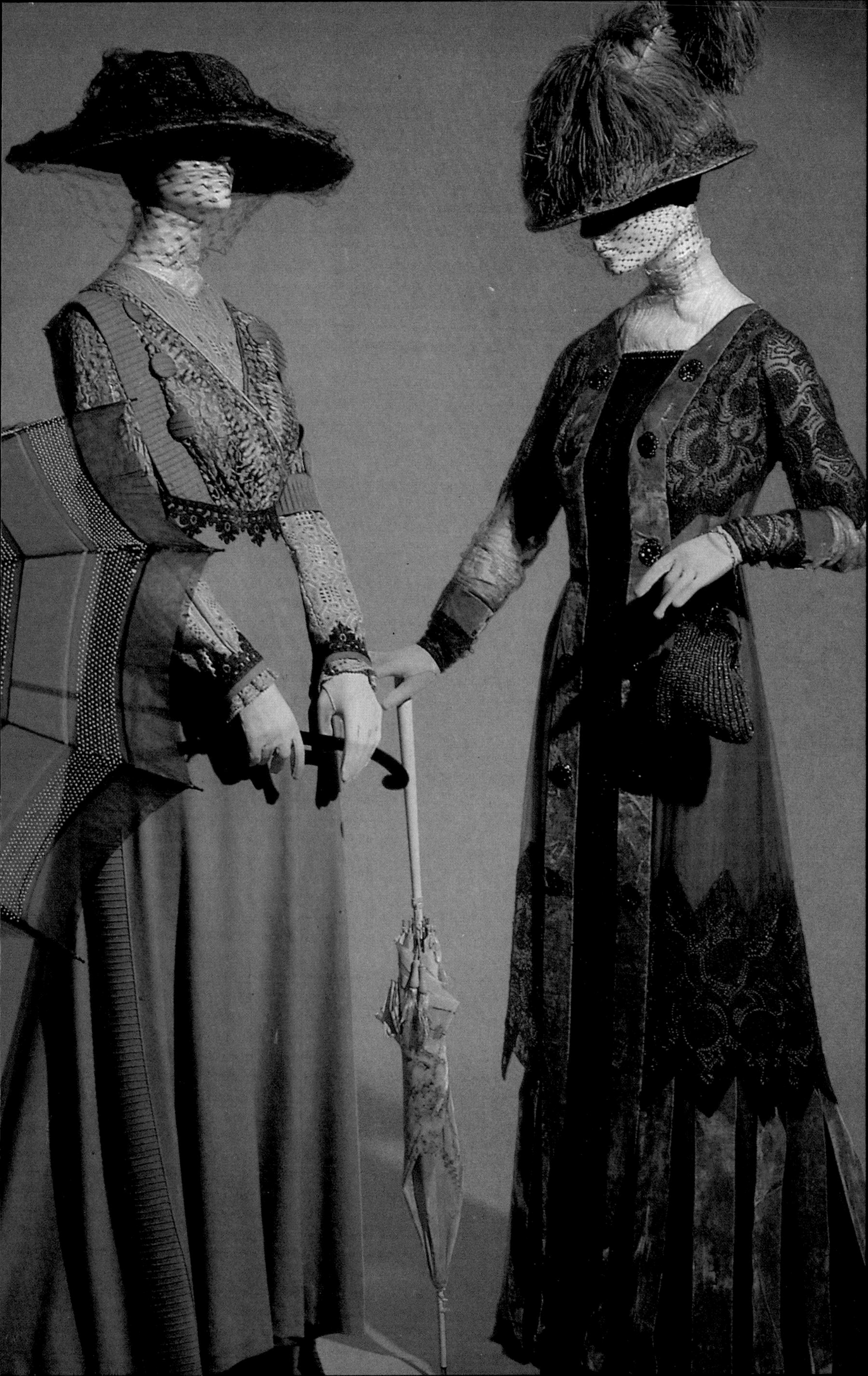

3. EVENING GOWN

Red – violet voided velvet patterned in design of ostrich plumes, trimmed with matching embroidered net and beads.
French, Circa 1910
Designed by Jean-Philippe Worth
Gift of Eva Drexel Dahlgren, 1976.258.7

WORTH, CHARLES FREDERICK (1826-95)

Worth was an Englishman. His family was not prosperous, and Charles Frederick was forced to leave formal education at the early age of eleven to seek gainful employment.
He served an apprenticeship as a salesboy with two London drapery firms where he acquired his business acumen. It was during this period that he frequented the nearby National Gallery to study the portraits of Van Dyck, Gainsborough and Velasquez, which later became so inspirational in his own work. In 1845 Worth moved to Paris and was engaged by the fashionable Gagelin and Opigez company. It was here that Worth first had an opportunity to show his flair for design, exhibiting his work at two world's fairs and setting up a made-to-order department within the company. He was the first to use a live mannequin, initially his wife, and popularized the collapsible steel version of the crinoline around 1855.
Leaving Gagelin in 1858, Worth opened a house in partnership with Bobergh. This enterprise closed during the Franco-Prussian War of 1870-71, to emerge solely as Maison Worth in 1874. Early in his career Worth contrived an introduction to the French court which propelled him to fame as dressmaker to the Empress Eugenie and her entourage. His house became notoriously expensive, and was unrivalled for the next fifty years. His gowns were made of beautiful and lavish amounts of fabric and were well-fitted. He promoted the 'Princess' cut, dresses with interchangeable parts, small bonnets which no longer shrouded the wearer's face.
A London branch was opened and 'Parfums Worth' introduced in 1900. Charles Frederick Worth was a man of great personal charm and tact who lived in grand style. After his death in 1895, the artistic direction was passed to his son Jean-Philippe, and Gaston who dealt with the administration and finance, later to be succeeded by his grandsons, until the house was sold in 1946.

4. EVENING GOWN

Dark emerald green figured ribbed silk and blue chiffon,
trimmed with dark blue and green beading and silver lace.
French, Circa 1913-14
Label: Jeanne Hallée
Gift of Mrs. David J. Colton, CI 64.7.5a

5. TEA GOWN

Pink silk shot with gold trimmed with cream colored lace, gold
metallic braid, pale blue satin and brown mink.
French, 1910
Label: Callot Soeurs
Gift of Mrs. Howard Crosby Brokaw, CI 60.42.6ab

HALLÉE, JEANNE

Although the house of Jeanne Hallée was apparently a very
prestigious establishment that flourished from the 1890s until
World War I, little information on Jeanne Hallée herself has
come to light. However, the number of dresses that have
survived attest to her popularity and bespeak the high quality
of her work. Like her contemporaries, Doucet, Beer and
Lanvin in the late 1890s and early 1900s Hallée turned
to the fashions of the 18th century for inspiration.
The appearance of the *Ballets Russes* in Paris in 1909
brought a strong flavor of the Orient to fashion. Hallée
embodied this new spirit and created clothes that reflected
Eastern forms and colors.

CALLOT SOEURS

The three Callot sisters were of Russian origin and daughters
of an antique dealer. They initially established their business
as a lace shop in Paris in 1895. The sisters shared with
another Parisian designer, Doucet, a love of the 18th-century
Rococo style. Taking chiffon, georgette, organdy, lace and
embroidery they created confections which were ultra-
feminine. One firm produced magnificent supple gold lamés
exclusively for their use. Proust was said to have criticized
their clothes as overly fussy. They enjoyed great success from
1916-26, and continued to be known even after the house
closed in 1935.

6. EVENING WRAP

Rose silk *faille* and black velvet with Oriental motifs
embroidered in multicolored silks, wool and beads; trimmed
with rose colored silk tassels.
French, 1912
Label: Paquin, Paris
Gift of Mrs. Edwin Stewart Wheeler, CI X56.2.1

PAQUIN

The house of Paquin opened in 1891 on the fashionable Rue
de la Paix, Paris. Its founder was Madame Joseph Paquin, the
wife of a prominent banker, who had trained at the early
Maison Rouff. Sound management and beautiful designs led
to the success of the house, and Madame Paquin became the
first woman since Rose Bertin to achieve importance in *haute
couture*. Acting as her own mannequin, she wore Paquin
gowns to society functions, and at the Paris Exposition of
1900 exhibited a wax figure of herself. She was the first
couturière to take groups of models to the opera and races,
and always concluded her shows with a tableau of girls
dressed in a blaze of white or palest green or gold. These
were her favorite colours, and from them she created
shimmering elegant evening gowns. Madame Paquin was
innovative in her use of fur as a trimming, and was also noted
for her blue serge suits enlivened with gold buttons and braid.
A skilled organizer, she endeavored to unite top French
dressmakers in world-wide promotions. She opened a house
in London in 1912 and later, branches in Madrid and Buenos
Aires. Her personal connection with the business ended in
1920, but the house of Paquin remained open until 1956.
Despite her public activities little is known of Madame
Paquin's background.

7. EVENING WRAP

Beige velvet with overall pattern of griffins and paisley-style motifs in shades of blue and olive green; trimmed with metallic braid.
French, Circa 1912
Label: Paul Poiret
Gift of the Kyoto Costume Institute, Koichi Tsukamoto, President Fund, 1980.86

8. DAY SUIT

Fine black wool broadcloth trimmed with silk stitching and
black silk cords.
French, 1911
Label: Martial Lépée, Paris
Gift of Miss Finn, CI 46.10.2ab

LÉPÉE, MARTIAL

In the early 20th century tailored clothes had gained such
importance in fashion that by the end of the first decade mos
couturiers included them in their collections. Smaller, lesser
known establishments, such as Martial Lépée, made suits of
especially fine quality.

9. HOODED EVENING CAPE

Mauve and grey striped velvet, made in the style of a North
African *burnouse.*
Italian, 20th century
Label: Mariano Fortuny
Gift of C.J. Vincente Minetti, 1972.209.28

9A. DELPHOS GOWN (worn under cape)

Pale grey-green pleated silk, sleeveles with scoop neckline
and Venetian beads.
Italian 20th century
Label: Mariano Fortuny
Gift of the Family of Mrs. M. Lincoln Schuster 177.363.4

10. DELPHOS GOWN

Dark olive green velvet stencilled in gold in a Middle Eastern
pattern edged in calligraphy: pleated black silk and Venetian
beads at sides.
Italian, 20th century
Label: Mariano Fortuny
Gift of Erna Obermeier, 1977.68.1

11. DELPHOS GOWN

Pink pleated silk, loose over-tunic and sleeves with Venetian
beads.
Italian, 20th century
Label: Mariano Fortuny
National Gallery of Victoria
Purchased 1977, D82. 1977

FORTUNY, MARIANO (1871-1949)

Mariano Fortuny Madrazo was born in Spain, the son of a
well-known painter. Fortuny's talents were threefold, as an
architect, an inventor and fashion creator. He devised a
unique method for the fine pleating and ombre tinting of
sheer silks which he made into exquisitely crafted and
beautiful gowns. His style was distinctly classic, a robe which
slipped over the head and tied simply with a cord at the waist.
He first showed his work in Venice around 1907, and later in
Paris. His technique never changed. Fortuny also printed
fabrics and stencilled velvets for his fashions as well as for use
in interior design. His dresses were considered status symbols
during the 1920s and 1930s and remain rare, expensive and
collectable items today.

12. EVENING GOWN

Deep pink satin with mauve floral pattern brocaded in gold
trimmed with purple net and gold lace.
French, 1916
Designed by Callot Soeurs
Gift of Agnes Miles Carpenter, CI 40.27.2

13. EVENING DRESS

Rose silk with silver metallic pattern, trimmed with silver
metallic lace, rose net, chiffon, beads and rhinestones.
French, 1916
Label: Callot Soeurs, Paris
Irene Lewisohn Bequest, CI 51.97.2

14. DINNER DRESS

Navy and red silk faille dress and matching poncho.
French, 1919
Designed by Paul Poiret
Gift of Muriel Draper, CI 43.85.2ab

POIRET, PAUL (1879-1944)

Paul Poiret was born to a cloth merchant family in Paris in 1879. The consuming interest of his youth was the theatre, a passion that was to have a profound effect on Poiret's designs. In 1896 he was engaged by Doucet where he had the chance to create costumes for the leading actresses of the time, Sarah Bernhardt and Réjane. Through this opportunity he gained recognition and great favor. After military service and a short period with Maison Worth, Poiret established his own business during 1904. Poiret brought vitality and vibrant colour back to women's fashion. A poineer in the use of oriental influences, he liberated women from their corsets and gave them high waistlines, flowing kimono tunics and billowing harem pants, but constrained them at the ankles with his restricting hobble skirts. His exotic embroideries and *aigrette*-adorned turbans were bright, exciting satellites of fashion. Paul Poiret was a traveller, a friend of Diaghilev and Bakst, and a patron of the arts. He established the Martine School of Decorative Arts in Paris and launched his own perfume 'Rosine', both named after his daughers. Sadly, as fashion moved from opulent to more practical styles of dress with the changing social conditions, Poiret did not.
He languished into ill-health, dying in near poverty and oblivion during April 1944.

15. DAY COAT

Black and white checked wool trimmed with large, mother-of
pearl buttons.
French, Circa 1916
Label: Bergdorf Goodman, New York
Gift of Chisholm Beach, CI 68.76.ab

16. COAT

Black ribbed silk and wool blend trimmed with pierced white
leather, collar of white ermine.
French, Circa 1918-1919
Label: Paul Poiret
Gift of Mrs. David J. Colton, CI 61.40.4

17. COAT

Ivory cashmere twill woven with wide floral patterned bands
in shades of brown.
French, Circa 1920
Label: Paul Poiret
Gift of Mrs. David J. Colton, CI 64.7.2.

18. EVENING DRESS

Matte black sequins, floral design of white opalescent sequins.
French, Circa 1925
National Gallery of Victoria
Purchased 1974, D 236.1974

19. EVENING DRESS

Black net, embroidered with silver, white beads, pink
spangles and black bugle beads.
French, Circa 1925
National Gallery of Victoria
Purchased 1977, D 86.1977

20. DANCING DRESS

Cream georgette sewn all over with iridescent paillettes; skirt has fringe of matching stripes.
French, Circa 1927
Designed by Molyneux
Gift of Mrs. Adam Gimbel, CI 42.33.3

21. EVENING DRESS

Black muslin embroidered all over with dark blue and gold sequins.
French, Circa 1927
National Gallery of Victoria
Purchased 1974, D 233.1974

MOLYNEUX, CAPTAIN EDWARD (1891-1974)

Edward Molyneux was an aristocrat of Huguenot descent, a fine sportsman, and a gifted artist born in Ireland. At the age of seventeen he joined the house of Lucile as a sketcher, working and travelling with that *couturière* until 1914. During the First World War Molyneux served as a Captain with the British Army, and unfortunately lost an eye. When the war was over he moved to Paris to resume his career, and opened his own house in 1919. He was an instant success and became couturier to many ladies, notably the Princess Marina, for whom he created a wedding dress and trousseau. Molyneux made alluring clothes, enhanced with a purity of line, that included printed silk suits with pleated skirts, tailored navy blue suits, coats and capes in his favourite soft shaded colors. He was a very superstitious man with a particular feeling for the number 5. He always opened his collections on the fifth day of the month and named his house perfume this. When World War II came Molyneux donated funds to the National Defence and did much work towards the war effort. In 1946 he resumed his place at the Paris house, expanding his business into furs, lingerie, millinery and perfumes. By 1950 his remaining sight was showing signs of failure, and he was forced to hand over the business to Jacques Griffe. He retired to his summer house in the warmer climate of Monte Carlo and, although he was persuaded to reopen in Paris in the January of 1965, this was a short interlude. He returned to the Riviera where he remained until his death in 1974.

22. EVENING DRESS (robe de style)

Black silk taffeta trimmed with silver beads, pearls and rhinestones.
French, 1926-1927
Label: Jeanne Lanvin
Gift of Mrs. Gilbert W. Chapman, 1976.30.la

23. EVENING DRESS (robe de style)

Pale golden yellow silk taffeta with embroidery of seed pearls, rhinestones, and gold beads.
American, Circa 1927
Label: Eldridge Manning
Gift of Mrs. Gerald F. Warburg, 1978.126

LANVIN, JEANNE (1867-1945)

Jeanne Lanvin initially designed and made hats of great originality which enabled her to establish a large clientele. She also enjoyed making clothes for her small daughter, and these were so eye-catching that her clients and friends ordered dresses for their own children. As the children grew up, so did Lanvin's designs. Her clothes had a unique style with a feeling for fantasy and a distinct flavour of the 18th and 19th centuries. Because of this charm they retained their popularity right through the boyish modes of the 1920s. Madame Lanvin's love of history and painting inspired her beautiful wedding and evening gowns, dolman wraps and capes enriched with fabulous embroideries. She was the maker of the Zouave bloomer suit in 1936. Lanvin's peak years were between the two World Wars. She always insisted on elegance and imported luxurious fabrics from the East. The artist, Paul Iribe, designed the Lanvin house symbol, a nostalgic emblem showing a small child tugging at the hands of its mother, which appears on the packaging of Lanvin perfumes 'My Sin' and 'Arpège'. Jeanne Lanvin was bestowed with many honors for her work and unanimously elected as a representative of French *couture* by her colleagues at many exhibitions, including the World's Fair in New York in 1939. Later the House of Lanvin opened branch shops in French resorts, and sold men's accessories and women's sports clothes and lingerie. On her death in 1945 the business passed to Lanvin's daughter, the Countess Jean de Polignac, who engaged Antonio del Castillo as designer. Since 1963 Jules François Crahay has designed for the House of Lanvin, but the business is still administered by family members.

MANNING ELDRIDGE

During the 1920s while Jeanne Lanvin was defying fashion trends in Paris with her romantic *robes de style,* the New York designer, Eldridge Manning, was flying the same flag on the other side of the Atlantic. His dresses showed pure nostalgia in their closely fitted and ornamented bodices and long skirts which poured onto the floor in yards of golden and pearl-hued silk. These flowing gowns of refined and subtle beauty had a special place in every woman's dreams. Eldridge Manning catered very successfully to this need.

24. LOUNGING PAJAMAS

Black and red faille crêpe embroidered with gold metallic
threads in diagonal bars; black silk pants
French, Circa 1929
Designed by Molyneux
Gift of Mrs. C.O. Kalman, 1979.569.17ab

25. LOUNGING PAJAMAS

Yellow crêpe de Chine printed in futuristic design in pinks,
blues and whites, trimmed with pink crêpe de Chine.
French, Circa 1926
Designed by Callot Soeurs
Gift of Mrs. Sidney G. Bernard, CI 44.64. 19a-d

26. AFTERNOON DRESS

Black satin-black crêpe trimmed with eggshell crêpe.
French, Circa 1928
Designed by Chanel
Gift of C.J. Vincente Minetti, 1972.209.27

27. SUIT

Dark brown and beige houndstooth checked wool, dark
brown wooden buttons.
French, Circa 1927
Label: Molyneux
Gift of Mrs. Georges Gudefin, CI 64.47.10ab

28. COAT

Brown and white tweed with collar of natural lynx.
American, 1928-29
Label: H. Jaeckel, New York
Gift of Mrs. Sidney G. Bernard, 1972.28.1

JAECKEL

The company of H. Jaeckel and Sons was established in
1863, situated at an exclusive address on New York's Fifth
Avenue. A furrier, Jaeckel was long revered as the finest in the
city both for the quality of the furs and for the excellent
tailoring and design. Jaeckel coats and wraps were created by
the house designers supplemented by a selection of the best
Paris models from each season. During the 1920s no
discerning woman would be without a Jaeckel sable or mink.
The company also kept a range of wool coats, each enhanced
by fur trimming and a choice of accessories.

29. SUMMER SUIT

Blue linen edged with matching linen knit.
French, 1937
Designed by Chanel
Gift of Diana Vreeland, CI 54.16.2ab

30. AFTERNOON DRESS

Bright red silk crêpe de Chine with white polka dots, trimmed with self-fabric corsage.
French, 1932
Designed by Mainbocher
Gift of Isabel Shults, CI 44.64.4ab

MAINBOCHER (1890-1976)

Main Rousseau Bocher grew up in Chicago as an aspiring opera singer. In 1917 he travelled to Europe with the intention of studying and developing his talents in art and music. Upon settling in Paris he worked as a sketcher for *Harpers Bazaar,* and in this field his career advanced quickly until he became the Fashion Editor for French *Vogue* in 1922, a post he held for seven years. In 1929 Mainbocher, as he called himself, decided to utilize his knowledge and skills in a different way and opened his own fashion house, becoming the first American to succeed as a dressmaker in France. He maintained this business until 1939 and achieved international fame in 1936 for designing the wedding gown and trousseau of the Duchess of Windsor, done in his own subtle color of 'Wallis blue'. Mainbocher returned to New York in 1940 opening a house there the following year. As a man of personal elegance and refinement he was a designer of great appeal to wealthy, conservative ladies. He was a master of understatement who believed in excellent cutting. Fabric was his luxury, both in quality and yardage. He is remembered for his beaded silk and fur-lined cardigans, corselet waists, strapless evening gowns, sleeveless day dresses and glamorous apron accessories for the 'little black dress'. Mainbocher designed for the theatre, and was also commissioned in 1942 to create a new uniform for the W.A.V.E.S., the U.S. Women's Navy, as well as a new Girl Scout uniform in 1948. He closed his salon in 1971 and returned to Europe where he spent his remaining years between homes in his favorite cities of Paris and Munich.

31. EVENING GOWN

Red machine made Chantilly lace.
French, Circa 1930
Designed by Chanel
Gift of Mrs. Carmel Snow, CI 56.26ab

32. EVENING GOWN

Claret-red silk velvet.
French, Circa 1929
Label: Madeleine Vionnet
Gift of Mrs. James Walter Carter,
1973.294.1a

33. EVENING GOWN

Purple machine-lace, worn over
purple satin slip.
French, 1930
Designed by Vionnet
Gift of Mrs. George C. Rand,
1979.575.1ab

34. EVENING ENSEMBLE

Black silk crêpe dress, trimmed with black ostrich feathers,
cape of black ostrich feathers.
French, Circa 1930
Designed by Chanel
Gift of Isabel Shults, CI 44.64.8abc

CHANEL, GABRIELLE 'COCO' (1883-1971)

Coco Chanel was born in the Auvergne region of France.
She came from humble beginnings, a fact she always denied
by taking great pains to conceal her age and origin, and even
by having her birth certificate altered. Her early career was
helped by her association with several influential men. She
started business in Paris with a hat shop in 1913 and opened
her couture house the following year. Chanel epitomized the
liberated woman, making famous her own boyish look and
adapting men's styles into something essentially feminine.
She bobbed her hair, and flaunted a suntan, which was
very trendsetting in the days of carefully preserved pearl
complexions. She became notable for wool jersey dresses
with neat white collar and cuffs, pea jeackets and bell-bottom
pants. She acquired the formula and launched her own
perfume, Chanel No. 5, in 1922. As part of the Paris clique of
artists and musicians she included among her close friends
Stravinsky, Cocteau and Diaghilev, for whom she designed
the costumes for *Le Train Bleu*. With the onset of war in 1939
Chanel closed her house, staying in seclusion until 1954. In
that year she made a triumphant return firmly establishing her
trademark, braid-edged cardigan suits of softest tweeds worn
with costume jewellery, artificial gardenias and slingback
pumps. Coco Chanel continued to work, building a vast
empire, and remained vital until her sudden death during the
preparation of her collection in 1971.

35. EVENING GOWN

Black silk crêpe.
French, Circa 1933
Designed by Mainbocher
Gift of Nancy S. Rosenfeld, CI 69.35.1

36. EVENING GOWN

Black satin, made completely on the bias and cinched at the waist with a carved white wooden buckle of an Art Deco stag.
French, 1937
Designed by Vionnet
Gift of Madeleine Vionnet, CI 52.18.2

VIONNET, MADELEINE (1876-1975)

Madeleine Vionnet can certainly be considered one of the greatest French *couturières* and one of the most influential designers the 20th century has seen. The daughter of a tax collector, she began dressmaking at the age of twelve, a skill in which she showed immense talent. She trained in London and in Paris under the guidance of Madame Gerber of Callot, and later joined the house of Doucet, where she introduced her revolutionary one-layer dresses with their wide, low necklines and total absence of inner construction. At the age of thirty-six she opened her own house, but, like so many *couturiers,* fell victim to the economies and stresses of running a business during a war. She managed to reopen in 1918 and was enormously successful for the next twenty years. During this time she personally draped and cut all her designs, modelling the fabrics and trying out her ideas on a small wooden mannequin. Vionnet was the innovator of the bias cut, a method which was then completely new and allowed for the tremendously supple and fluid lines which epitomize a Vionnet gown. She used the finest, softest velvets, crêpe-de-Chines and satins to achieve her almost classic look in clothes that were easy to wear and had a minumum of fastenings. She liked cowl and halter necklines, and decorated her clothes simply with fagotted seams and Art Deco embroideries. Her cut and style are difficult to imitate but attempts have been made by designers all over the world ever since. Vionnet was very helpful to her protégés who included, notably, Pierre Balmain, Jacques Griffe and Marcelle Chaumont. In 1929 she was awarded the French Legion d'Honneur in recognition of her contribution to fashion. Retiring in 1939, she remained in Paris in close touch with the fashion world for the rest of her life.

37. EVENING CAPE

Black velvet, embroidered with gold metallic sequins, gold
bugle beads, gold bullion and amber paste in design of
Versailles' Fountain of Neptune.
French, 1938
Designed by Schiaparelli
Gift of Estate of Lady Mendi, CI 51.83

38. EVENING GOWN

Accordian pleated lamé with rainbow colored panels
sprinkled with silver paillettes.
French, Circa 1937
Designed by Vionnet
Gift of Mrs. Byron C. Foy, 53.40.1

SCHIAPARELLI, ELSA (1890-1973)

Elsa Schiaparelli was an Italian, born in Rome to an
intellectual family. She married as a teenager, and moved to
New York with her husband. Unfortunately the marriage was
unsuccessful and Elsa, with a small daughter to support,
started to knit sweaters to supplement her income. In 1929
she went to Paris and set up a small attic workshop and
knitwear business. It was not long before her unusual
creations caught attention and a demand grew for her work.
Probably her most famous and sensational sweater was the
trompe l'oeil black silk pullover with knitted-in white bow tie.
Schiaparelli opened her first boutique in 1935 and added
dresses to her range. Her evening gowns and matching
jackets, with their wide, exaggerated shoulders, unusual
decoration and nipped waists, soon became the rage of Paris.
Schiaparelli moved among the Parisian elite in a circle in
which it was fashionable to be outrageous. Her signature
colour, shocking pink, her 'Shocking' perfume and her *avant
garde* accessories gave rise to the expression 'hard chic'. An
extensive traveller, Schiaparelli drew many of her ideas from
the native costumes which she discovered *en route*. The first
couturière to experiment with synthetic fibres, she also
commissioned Salvador Dali to design surrealist prints for her
fabrics. During World War II Schiaparelli stopped designing,
but reopened in 1945 with a collection of timeless black
dresses. Finally retiring in 1954, she published her
autobiography, appropriately entitled *Shocking Life,* and
remained a consultant to her business until her death.

39. DINNER OR THEATRE SUIT

Black velvet trimmed white linen, and mother-of-pearl
buttons.
French, 1939
Designed by Chanel
Gift of Mrs. John Chambers Hughes, CI 58.34.22ab

40. EVENING COSTUME

Black velvet jacket; trimmed with gold tinsel, mirror and black
plastic buttons in shape of women's heads.
French, 1939
Label: Schiaparelli
Gift of Baroness Philippe de Rothschild, CI 50.34.2

41. EVENING ENSEMBLE

Silk crêpe in shades of brown taupe, moss green, maroon
and light blue arranged in a Picasso style pattern.
American, 1945
Designed by Adrian
Gift of Eleanor Lambert, CI 58.25a -c

ADRIAN – Gilbert Adrian Greenburgh (1903-59)

The work of the American designer, Adrian, will be known to
millions of people although his name will not always be
familiar. After studying at the Paris branch of the Parsons
School of Design, he went into the theatre and became a
costume designer for Broadway productions. In 1923 he
moved to the M.G.M. film studios, and it was there that he
gained his reputation as Hollywood's top designer and
reigned supreme for sixteen years. Adrian created the wide
and exaggerated padded shoulders for, actress, Joan
Crawford, and he poured Jean Harlow into the slinky dresses
which became her hallmark. These were ideas which had an
immense impact on world fashion at all levels. His *couture*
and ready-to-wear salon in Los Angeles opened in 1942, and
in 1944 he received the Coty award for fashion. Adrian
sparked new attitudes toward fabrics when he used checked
gingham for tailored suits. His interest in modern and
Egyptian art influenced his designs, and his love of wildlife
was manifest in fierce jungle animals prowling across sinuous
black evening gowns. Adrian's gift was to surprise his public
with fashions that were always dramatic and always new.
Stepping out of the limelight, he retired to Brazil in 1952 and
devoted his time to painting landscapes.

43. AFTERNOON ENSEMBLE

Gold and black melton cloth with black gabardine.
American, 1946-47
Designed by Philip Mangone
Gift of Bloomingdale Brothers, Inc., CI 47.74.4a -c

MANGONE, PHILIP

Philip Mangone's father was a tailor in one of the European courts. It was later, when his father had moved to a workroom in New York, that Philip became an apprentice learning the finer points of cutting and draping. At the age of nineteen he was employed by a tailoring company and sent to Paris. By the time he was twenty-seven he was the head of his own business. Mangone became a master of his art, renowned for his use of fabrics and clever fur trimmings and linings. His superbly made coats and suits had a wonderful fit that was never rigid or unfeminine. Although he began to design in the 1920s, his greatest success came during the 1940s.

44. 'NEW LOOK' COCKTAIL DRESS

Black wool, shaped fitted bodice and wide skirt over full black
taffeta petticoat.
French, 1947-48
Designed by Christian Dior
Gift of Mrs. Byron C. Foy, CI 53.40.16ab

45. H-LINE EVENING COSTUME

Fine black wool broadcloth trimmed with black satin.
French, 1954
Designed by Christian Dior
Gift of Christian Dior, CI 55.29.2ab

46. A-LINE SPRING SUIT

Banker's grey silk and wool flannel.
French, 1955
Designed by Christian Dior
Gift of Christian Dior, CI 55.63a-c

DIOR, CHRISTIAN (1905-57)

The son of a wealthy French industrialist, Dior originally
studied for a diplomatic career. When he completed his
education, however, he opened an art gallery and spent
much time travelling overseas. By 1935 he was selling his
fashion illustrations to *Le Figaro Illustré* and sketching hats
for Agnès. This exposure brought him a post with Piguet
in 1938 as an assistant designer, and in 1941 he moved
to Lucien Lelong. Backed by the textile magnate, Marcel
Boussac, Dior was able to become independent. He opened
his own house on the Avenue Montaigne, Paris, in Febuary
1947, and enjoyed instant acclaim for his 'New Look'. This
ultra-feminine silhouette, with a long full skirt, snug bodice
and tiny waist, was truly stunning to a public accustomed to
shortages and wartime fashions. With this first collection Dior's
name was carved into the annals of fashion history. During
the next ten years Dior devised his cleverly constructed
H, A and Y lines, and had great commercial success. His
business quickly expanded into accessories, perfumes, and
the younger, less expensive 'Miss Dior' range. Dior was
a modest, introverted and superstitious man, with a passion
for 19th-century painting. He always withdrew to his country
residence to design his collections in peaceful seclusion. At his
early death in 1957 his young assistant, Yves Saint Laurent,
took over design for the House of Dior. Later Marc Bohan
assumed responsibility.

47. SACK-BACK DAY DRESS

Dark brown wool jersey.
French, 1955-56
Designed by Balenciaga
Gift of Muriel Rand, CI 64.4.3

48. SUIT

Navy blue wool jersey, tucked white muslin blouse with black velvet bow, sailor hat of navy straw.
French, 1954
Designed by Chanel
Gift of Bettina Ballard, CI 58.7.9a-g

49. COAT DRESS

Grey bouclé wool, in 'trapeze' style
French, 1958
Designed by Yves Saint-Laurent for Christian Dior
Gift of Imogene Schubert, CI 58.66ab

SAINT LAURENT, YVES (b1936)

Yves Saint Laurent was born and educated in French Algeria, a country where his family had lived for several generations. An immensely shy and unassuming youth, Yves spent much of his free time sketching and dreaming of a theatrical career. In 1953 he won a design prize for a black asymetrically-cut cocktail dress which brought him to Paris, and the subsequent publicity secured him a job as a fashion illustrator with French *Vogue.* He continued to produce his own designs which he showed to Christian Dior, who immediately hired him as an assistant designer. Dior was already an unwell man, and at his death in 1957 Yves Saint Laurent inherited the top design post, a remarkable achievement for one so young. The 'trapeze' line of his first solo collection was a fantastic success. However, his next presentation, the 'Beat' look, was out of line with expectation and the resulting controversy brought a rift with the Dior administration. In 1960 Saint Laurent was given time out for army duty and illness and he did not return, but instead opened his own house in 1962. Some of his memorable designs are the pea jackets, Mondrian-inspired dresses of 1965 with their bold blocks of primary color, his casual safari pants-suits, and the naughty 'nude' look of 1966. This same year saw the opening, with his partner Pierre Bèrge, of the first 'Rive Gauche' boutique, and the creation of the perfume 'Y'. In the 1970s Saint Laurent's sustained interest in the theatre showed in his Russian and 'rich peasant' collections of 1977. He was considered almost anti-*couture* and did design for the French stage and revue. Yves Saint Laurent has kept his boyish appearance, belying his age. Although still reserved, he is a highly articulate man. In spite of the earlier inconsistencies in design and his wavering press, he is now a highly acclaimed and influential designer catering to the young and sophisticated woman. His 'Rive Gauche' boutiques sell male and female ready-to-wear in branches world-wide.

50. WINTER COAT

Cranberry colored mohair.
American, 1951
Designed by Charles James
Gift of Eleanor Searle Whitney McCollum, 1975.246.1

51. EVENING GOWN

Black wool jersey, backless, halter top.
French, 1952
Designed by Givenchy for Schiaparelli
Gift of Mrs. Daisy Eric, 1973.52b

52. BALLGOWN

Shocking pink satin bodice trimmed with black bead
embroidery, black silk faille skirt.
French, Circa 1950
Label: Schiaparelli
Gift of Alma de Luce, 1975.139.lab

GIVENCHY, HUBERT (b1927)

Hubert Givenchy began his fashion career at the age of
seventeen, working for Jacques Fath. He also spent time with
Piguet and Lelong before joining Elsa Schiaparelli, where he
assisted in designing separates for four years. He decided
to branch out on his own, although he had little money to
decorate an expensive salon or purchase fine fabrics. He took
a gamble and showed his first solo collection, a range of
separates made from inexpensive cottons, in the winter
of 1952. Scepticism gave way to excitement and his designs
became best sellers the following summer. By the late 1950s
Givenchy had moved to larger premises and a fashionable
address, close to Balenciaga whom he greatly admired.
His later *couture* shows a distinct influence from this master,
with bold statements of shape and sober color.

53. OPERA COAT

Black velvet, puffed gathers over trumpet flared skirt.
American, 1956
Designed by Charles James
Gift of Lord and Taylor, CI 57.27

JAMES, CHARLES (1906-78)

Charles James was born in England and educated at Harrow.
His father was an army officer and the whole family moved
to Chicago with their father's posting. James set out to design
hats, but moved back to Europe and opened dressmaking
salons in London during the 1920s and in Paris during
the 1930s. He was not a master of administration and his
businesses ended in failure. However, he is regarded as
a gifted designer and his work has found its way into many
museum collections. Innovative in shape and cutting
techniques, his dresses, like artworks, were commissioned by
famous women and took months to complete. His gowns had
heavily reinforced substructures that created a shape of their
own which had little dependence upon the figure of the
wearer. Charles James retired from *couture* design in 1958.
He acted as consultant to teaching and design projects during
the early 1960s. Later until his death in 1978, he
concentrated on painting and sculpture.

54. EVENING DRESS

Short sheath covered with with ruched black net dotted with
black velvet, balloon style overskirt of grey-blue faille.
French, Circa 1959
Designed by Balenciaga
Gift of Inge Morath Miller, 1973.147.1ab

55. EVENING DRESS

Short black taffeta sheath with blue taffeta draped in front
over bodice and in accordion pleats over skirt ending in pouf
at hem
French, Circa 1957
Designed by Grès
Gift of Mrs. Murray Graham, CI 61.39.4

GRÈS, ALIX

A contemporary of Vionnet, Alix Grès was originally a
sculptress. Her clothes are a testament to this, for she drapes
and manipulates fabric into monuments of fashion. Following
an apprenticeship with Premet she showed *toiles* under her
own name, Alix (Barton), in 1934. By 1942 she had married
and opened her own house using her husband's name, Grès.
Her first collection, presented during wartime, was defiantly
shown in red, white and blue. The German occupation closed
her down, but when she reopened in 1945 Madame Grès
became famous for her superb craftsmanship and exquisitely
sculptural clothes, which attracted an avid following in Europe
and America. Along with Chanel she reinstated jersey as an
acceptable fashionable fabric, using silk for evening and wool
for day. True to her original skill she literally models each dress
directly onto the mannequin with a minumum of cutting, and
moulds the fabric to enhance the body. She achieves a
statuesque look with a subtle blend of neutral colors, fine
pleats, asymetric drapery, hoods and batwing sleeves.
The Grès house perfume is 'Cabochard'. A retiring,
enigmatic personality, Madame Grès became President of
the Chambre Syndicale de la Couture Parisienne in 1972.
She continues to be a profound influence and figurehead
of 20th-century fashion.

56. EVENING WRAP (KABUKI)

Deep rose-pink silk faille.
French, 1954-55
Designed by Balenciaga
Gift of Baroness Philippe de Rothschild, 1973.21.3

BALENCIAGA, CRISTOBAL (1895-1972)

Cristobal Balenciaga grew up in a small Spanish fishing village. His father was a boat captain and his mother a seamstress. When he was fourteen years old he made a copy of a Paris suit. His accomplishment was noticed by a wealthy local lady who encouraged him to leave home to study design, and who offered to patronize his training. She also financed his first business in San Sebastian. Soon he had expanded to branches in Madrid and Barcelona and was designing under the name 'Eisa'. Discouraged by the Spanish Civil War, Balenciaga moved to Paris where he opened a house in 1937, with immediate success. Considered a perfectionist, Balenciaga was one of the few *couturiers* who could design, cut, sew and fit the whole garment. He is revered by many as a master who had great influence on the 20th-century fashion, numbering Givenchy, Courrèges and Ungaro among those who worked under him. Balenciaga's styles changed slowly from one season to the next with a predominating thread of brown and black color. His innovations included the prophetic 'sack' silhouette of 1953, the 'middy' dress which evolved into a chemise in 1955, and the pill-box hat. A recluse, Balenciaga avoided publicity, except that which promoted his perfumes. The gradual decline of elegance brought increasing disillusionment to the *couturier* and he retired in 1968. He emerged once to design the wedding dress of General Franco's granddaughter, but died two months later, aged 77. He is buried in his native town.

57. EVENING GOWN

White silk matte jersey trimmed with gold lamé ribbons.
French, 1950
Designed by Grès
Gift of Mrs. Byron C. Foy, CI 56.60.6a

58. BALLGOWN

Blue satin with overall pattern of large rose sprigs in varying
shades of blue.
French, 1954
Designed by Christian Dior
Gift of Mrs. Byron C. Foy, CI 56.60.7

59. SHORT EVENING DRESS

Peach colored silk faille.
French, 1958
Label: Christian Dior
Gift of Mrs. Hugh J. Chisholm, Jr., CI 68.1

60. EVENING ENSEMBLE

White organdy blouse; black alligator leather slacks.
American, 1963
Designed by Scaasi
Gift of Mrs. Bruce Addison, CI 68.31 and
Gift of Scaasi, Inc., CI 64.3

61. SHORT COCKTAIL ENSEMBLE

Acid green silk marquisette.
French, 1966
Designed by Balenciaga
Gift of Claudia-Antoinette de Osborne, 1974.237.3ab

62. EVENING GOWN

Three shades of green silk chiffon.
French, 1966-67
Label: Grès
Gift of Mrs. Frederick A. Melhado, 1970.152.1

63. AT-HOME COSTUME

Silk satin patterned with exotic motifs in multicolored chiné
and gilt threads.
French, 1964-65
Label: Grès
Gift of Mrs. Frederick A. Melhado, 1970.152.2

SCAASI, ARNOLD (b1931)

Canadian-born Arnold Scaasi is one of America's last existing
custom designers. Originally called Isaacs, he reversed the
spelling of his name to give it the more exotic sound which
he prefers. He studied in Paris and worked for Paquin before
returning to the fashion district of New York, where he joined
Charles James. Scaasi opened his own wholesale business in
1956, and has had a custom salon since 1963. His speciality is
the creation of dramatic evening clothes in luxurious fabrics,
lavished with fur or feathers and intricately cut, that appeal
to a very glamourous market.

64. EVENING ENSEMBLE

Black rose patterned lace.
French, 1965
Label: Balenciaga
Gift of Mrs. Charles B. Wrightsman, CI 67.53.4ab

65. LATE AFTERNOON DRESS

Black wool crêpe trimmed with black fox.
American, 1967
Designed by Norman Norell
Gift of Teal Traina, CI 68.24.abf

NORELL, NORMAN (1900-72)

Norman Norell grew up as Norman Levinson, the son of an Indiana haberdasher. Like so many great designers he studied at the Parsons School of Design in New York, and worked for a short period as a movie and theatre costume designer. Moving into commercial fashion, he worked for Charles Armour from 1924-28, and for Hattie Carnegie until 1941. In that year he formed the memorable Traina/Norell partnership, but it was not until Traina's death in 1960 that Norell had his own independent company. Universally regarded as one of America's top designers, he was the first to be elected to the Hall of Fame by Coty award judges in 1958. He is known for precision tailoring, and was the first to incorporate *couture* techniques and quality into ready-to-wear clothing. The recurring features in his collections were the understated jersey dresses, the chemise 'no-waistline' dress, pussycat bow blouses under double-breasted coats, and spectacular sequinned sheaths for evening. Athough he never followed fads, he maintained a penchant for nautical detail, and held an enduring admiration for the work of Balenciaga, Vionnet and Chanel. In1968 Revlon launched the Norell perfume. On 15 October 1972, the eve of his fifty-year retrospective show at the Metropolitan Museum of Art in New York, Norman Norell tragically suffered a stroke from which he did not recover.

66. EVENING GOWN

American Beauty chiffon over layers of bright pink chiffon.
American, 1967
Label: Galanos
Gift of Galanos, CI 68.19.4a

67. EVENING GOWN

Red, orange, yellow and gold chiffon trimmed with
multicolored iridescent paillettes.
French, 1967
Label: Christian Dior
Gift of Joanne T. Cummings, 1976.360.14ab

GALANOS, JAMES (b1925)

Galanos was born James Gorgoliatos of American-Greek
parentage. His primary fashion studies were undertaken in
New York, but 1947 found him in Paris where he trained for
a further three years with Robert Piguet, along with a
contemporary, Marc Bohan. Upon his return to America in
1951, Jean Louis assisted Galanos in starting a business in
Los Angeles. His first showing in New York in 1953 was the
milestone which finally launched him on a career as one of
the greatest, most independent designers in the United States.
Using European fabrics and creating intuitively, Galanos
works on a model, without sketching, designing a total look.
He is best known for his superb handling of chiffon in
floating evening dresses and for his very rich use of beading
and embroidery. His dresses are worn by many famous
personalities. The winner of many design awards during the
1950s, he is still based in California.

68. BATHING SUIT

Deep burgundy rayon twill.
French, 1949
Designed by Schiaparelli
Gift of A.M. Tenney Associates Inc. and
Tennesse Eastman Corp., CI 50.21.3

69. BATHING SUIT

Black wool jersey, made in a diaper style.
American, 1944
Designed by Claire McCardell
Gift of Claire McCardell, CI 49.37.19

70. BATHING SUIT AND COAT

Navy blue wool striped in white, cream colored wool belt
with silver buckle.
French, 1929-30
Label: Hermès, Paris
Gift of Mrs. Sidney Bernard, CI 56.33.17a-c

HERMÈS

This Paris firm originated in 1837 as Thierry Hermès, saddler
and harness maker, supplying the crowned heads of Europe.
The business was passed down through the family, and over
the years accessories, toilet articles, boots and jewellery were
added to create the Hermès House of Leather and Fashion.
The Hermès hallmark scarf, still in production, retains the
'horsey' theme of the company printed on silk. A grandson of
the founder, Emile Hermès, took complete control in 1920
and updated the designs. He was the first to incorporate
zippers into handbags and luggage. The *couture* side was
started primarily with leather garments, sweaters, capes and
shoes. Later, ready-to-wear Hermès Sport was introduced in
a new store. The only one of its kind, it had an entire floor
given over to a museum display of historic sporting and travel
goods. Hermès now has branches in major cities, world-wide
under fifth-generation directorship, and is famous for
'Calèche' perfume.

71. BLOOMER PLAYSUIT

Red, blue, yellow, green and white plaid cotton.
American, 1942
Designed by Claire McCardell
Gift of Claire McCardell, CI 49.37.46

McCARDELL, CLAIRE (1906-58)

Claire McCardell was one of American fashion's great
innovators. She studied in Paris and at the Parsons School of
Design in New York. Claire McCardell held her own view of
fashion which did not always match the mainstream, even
when working for Hattie Carnegie and Townley. Because her
clothes were initially considered unconventional her career
got off to a slow start, but once this barrier had been broken
she was hailed as the top U.S. designer throughout the 1940s
and 1950s. McCardell was the creator of the 'American look'
with day-long, any occasion clothes that were casual and
easy fitting, while at the same time elegant and imaginative.
She gathered ideas from many sources, including basic work
clothes, and often used functional closures as ornaments for
a dress. Among her many firsts are the bias-cut belted 'tent'
dress, the diaper bathing suit of 1942, the denim popover
housedress of 1943, and fabric ballet slippers for outdoor
wear in 1944. Her concept of interchangeable separates
was inspired by her own travel needs. Her untimely death
in 1958 ended a still flourishing career.

72. SPORTS ENSEMBLE

Black wool jumper with red leather belt; leotards and blouse
of striped red, black and brown wool jersey.
American, 1943
Designed by Claire McCardell
Gift of Claire McCardell, CI 49.37.11a-d

73. TRAVEL COSTUME 'THE ORIGINAL FLIGHT SUIT'

Brown and white Irish tweed and cocoa brown jersey, coat
has plastic lined pockets for such objects as toothbrush,
toothpaste, washcloth, etc.
American, 1948
Designed by Vera Maxwell
Gift of Vera Maxwell, CI 53.61 a-c

74. APRES-SKI ENSEMBLE

Green and grey knit wool, cocoa beige stretch nylon,
matching leather belt, cape of lime green fake fur.
French, 1967
Designed by Balenciaga
Gift of Claudia-Antoinette de Osborne, 1974.237.4a-d

MAXWELL, VERA (b1904)

Vera Maxwell, an American, trained as a ballet dancer and
became interested in design while working as a part-time
model. She is acknowledged as a craftswoman, and a highly
original designer uninfluenced by the dictates of Paris. She
worked first with sportswear and coat firms before opening
her own business in New York. Her first big success was with
a classic riding jacket, revamped for the street and worn with
a grey flannel skirt. She believes in classic mix and match
separates using the finest quality fabrics, including Scottish
tweeds, wool jersey and raw silk. Her inspiration has often
been found in men's tailoring and fabrics. Noteworthy in her
career are her 'weekend wardrobe' of 1935, the Chesterfield
coat and slacks, wrap-tie blouses, and the braid-edged
mandarin coat with slit sides. Vera Maxwell, who loves opera,
ballet and travel, was honored by a retrospective show at the
Smithsonian Institution, Washington, D.C., in 1970.

75. MINI DRESS

Red-purple wool trimmed with white jersey.
English, 1966-67
Designed by Mary Quant
Gift of Mrs. Maxine Mckendry, CI 69.10.1

76. COAT DRESS

White wool twill bound with navy grosgrain.
French, 1965
Label: Courrèges
Gift of Kimberly Knitwear, Inc., 1974.136.3

77. DAY DRESS

Wool jersey made of geometric segments in white, red, and blue, separated by bars of black, à la Mondrian.
French, 1965
Label: Yves Saint Laurent
Gift of Mrs. William Rand, CI 69.23

QUANT, MARY (b1934)

Mary Quant is a British designer who trained at Goldsmiths College in London, where she met her husband and business partner, Alexander Plunkett-Greene. Together, in the mid-1950s, they opened the shop 'Bazaar' on a shoestring budget, and are credited with starting the whole 'Chelsea' and 'Mod' look. Their success lay in the fact that theirs was the first shop to appeal directly to and cater exclusively for the newly emerged, independent and highly spirited youth. Quant clothes were unconventional. Her tight pants, shaggy sweaters and thick knitted stockings, boyish knickerbockers and notorious 'mini' skirts, were just what the young were looking for in a style of their own. She used utility fabrics such as denim, colored flannels and vinyls, and made them exciting by her design. Her trademark was the daisy motif. The business expanded with great rapidity, and a cheaper 'Ginger Group' range was added. Quant cosmetics were launched in 1966. She invented the craze for 'hot-pants' in 1970. Now Mary Quant designs furnishings, fabrics and accessories, which are marketed by large companies under her name.

COURRÈGES, ANDRE (61923)

Andre Courrèges studied civil engineering before fashion and textile design, a combination which provided the basis for his functional clothes with their unique architectural proportions. Courrèges also worked as chief fitter for Balenciaga between 1952 and 1960, and his designs have been influenced by this experience. He has been labelled the *couturier* of the space age, the producer of 'tough chic'. It is easy to recall his all-white collections that showed dresses above the knee in crisp squared lines, tunics over narrow pants worn with flat white boots, industrial zippers and slit-eyed sunglasses. His shows are exciting and fast-moving, mirroring the designer's own personality. In 1965 Courrèges sold his business, and retired to dress only his private clients. He returned in 1967 with a sheer 'naked' look and knitted cat-suits, which again placed him in the forefront of fashion design. By 1972 his collection showed much more femininity. Evening gowns were shown in pink and softened with ruffles, and the pants were loose and comfortable. The following year his menswear range was introduced, and today the Courrèges ready-to-wear boutiques are international.

78. EVENING MINI DRESS

Black organza piped in a lattice pattern over tan silk, trimmed with black vinyl.
French, 1967
Label: Courrèges
Gift of Jane Holzer. 1977.115.13

79. DANCE DRESS

Raspberry pink silk crêpe.
French, 1966-67
Label: Pierre Cardin
Gift of Mrs. William Rand, 1975.145.7

80. DRESS

Gilded plastic rectangles and squares joined by metal links.
French, 1966
Designed by Paco Rabanne
Gift of Jane Holzer, 1974.384.33

CARDIN, PIERRE (b1922)

Pierre Cardin began his career as an assistant to Paquin and Schiaparelli, before heading the Dior workroom in 1947. In 1950 Cardin opened his own business, 'Adam and Eve', with designs for women and a range of ties, vests and sweaters for men. His first success came in 1957 when he showed innovative fashions in the *avant garde* of *couture*. Cardin, originally a student of architecture, has always been fascinated by technology and geometric and irregular shapes. His experiments with barrel skirts cartridge pleated wool, scalloped edgings and appliqués brought him acclaim as one of the 1950s and 60s most creative *couturiers*. In 1958 he expanded his concept of menswear into unisex bodysuits, worn with helmets and boots, and belted with his trademark metal buckles. The 1970s saw the expansion of his business to include perfumes, environmental and product designs.

RABANNE, PACO (b1934)

A Spaniard, Paco Rabanne is the son of Balenciaga's chief dressmaker. Although his studies in Paris were in architecture, he began to design plastic fashion accessories and from there moved to clothes design. Rabanne opened his own fashion house in Paris in 1966, causing a sensation with metal-linked plastic disc dresses, feather extravaganzas with plastic link straps, sun-goggles and jewellery in primary colors. His designs are stark and futuristic. His methods of moulding and welding, instead of sewing, were considered remarkable and new. Rabanne carried the linked-disc theme into his later fur-patched coats, leather-patched dresses, and masses of buttons laced together with wire of aluminum strips. He also pioneered synthetic suede dresses in 1970. The Rabanne signature perfume is 'Calandre'. Over the last few years Paco Rabanne has concentrated his energies more upon environmental design.

ACCESSORIES

87 FAN European early 20th century (detail)

81 SHOE

Bronzed kid with geometric cut-out design, high button
vamp.
American, circa. 1908
Label: Oppenheim Collins & Co.,
Gift of Henry F. Green, CI 63.45.2a

82 BONNET

Navy blue straw and raffia, trimmed with orange velvet
ribbon and a pink velvet flower,
French, circa. 1909
Designed by Carlier, Paris
Gift of the Estate of Annie-May Hegeman. CI 50.40.15

83 SHOE

Beige satin brocaded in multicolored floral pattern with
rhinestone buckle.
French, circa. 1913
Gift of Howard Sturges, CI 49.2.6b

84 TOQUE

Pale pink straw trimmed with pink and lavender lilacs and five
purple iris.
French, 1913-1914
Designed by Caroline Reboux
Gift of Mrs. Andrew Winton Roth, CI 59.22

85 PURSE

Royal and navy blue beads with crystal border and floral
pattern, strap handles and looped tassel trim; purse is square
in shape when laid flat.
Belgian, 1914
Gift of Mrs. George A. Spiegelberg, CI 66.162

86 SHOE

Green leather with Louis XV heel and velvet buckle.
French, circa. 1915
Label: Hellestern & Sons, Paris
Anonymous gift, CI 44.52.8a

87 FAN

Amber yellow guinea hen feathers.
European, early 20th century.
Gift of Mrs. Janos Scholz, 1978.583.8

88 FAN

Eagle feathers.
American, early 20th century
Gift of Mrs. Janos Scholz, 1978.583.38

89 FAN

Mother-of-pearl guards, ivory sticks; leaf of ivory Brussels and
rosepoint lace.
American, early 20th century
Designed by Tiffany & Co.
Gift of Millia Davenport, CI X62.5.14

90 DAY BOOT

Russet calf and gold kidskin trimmed with snakeskin.
Belgian, early 20th century
Label: Saks, Herald Square, Made in Belgium
Gift of Karl M. Stone, CI 48.69.38a

91 HANDBAG

Grey suede printed in a stylized foliage motif in blue
embroidered in cut steel beads with applied blue stone beetle
on one side.
French (?), early 20th century
Gift of Thomas Nichol Jr., CI 60.13.7

92 GLOVE

Black satin embroidered in seed pearls and gold thread,
shoulder length.
French, early 20th century
Designed by Suzanne Talbot
Gift of Mrs. Ector Munn. CI 46.4.9a

93 HANDBAG

Cocoa-colored suede, front and back covered with plaques
inlaid with engraved mother-of-pearl and brass wires
depicting swans and flowers.
European, 20th century
Gift of Mrs. Stephen M. Kellen, 1978.165.10

89 FAN American early 20th century (detail)

94 FAN

Orange feathers.
American, 1920s
Gift of Mrs. B. Brewster Jennings, 1977.151.11

95 EVENING SHOE

Silver kidskin with stencilled geometric design in
pink and blue.
American, circa 1925
Gift of Mrs. R.C. Jacobsen, CI 54.14.2b

96 HANDBAG

Golden yellow brocade with enamelled Art Deco frame set
with marcasites.
French, circa 1965
Label: Jane Saltati, Paris
Gift of Julia B. Henry, 1978.288.41

97 PURSE

Tan leather with semi-transparent celluloid set with tiny
stones, in floral design edged with gold.
French, circa 1928
Gift of Miss Irene Lewisohn and Mrs Alice Lewisohn Crowley,
CI 46.9.124

98 PURSE

Gold metal frame with pouch of faceted red plastic beads.
American, 1928
Gift of Madame Lilliana Teruzzi, 1972.30.20

99 SLIPPER

Off-white kid with pale-blue lizard trim and buckle of blue and
gold enamel.
American, circa 1928
Gift of Mrs. Peter A. Cohn, CI 53.39b

100 GLOVE

White kid with wide flaring gauntlet cuff edged in scallops and
pierced blue kid.
French, late 1920s early 1930s
Designed by Alexandrine, Paris
Irene Lewisohn Bequest 1976.148.8a

101 HANDBAG

Black cloth pouch on silver frame, encrusted with
rhinestones, lined with silver lame.
French, circa 1934
Gift of Mrs. Byron C. Foy

102 HANDBAG

Black silk faille; bronze flap with cut-out floral design.
American, 1935
Gift of Milton S. Graber, CI 54.24.8

103 EVENING JACKET

Black velvet, with front edges and hem bound in graduated
silver cording, accented with clusters of pearly pink and white
plastic flowers, magenta sequins and pearls.
French, circa 1937
Designed by Schiaparelli
Gift of Julia B. Henry, 1978.288.21a

104 HANDBAG

Black velvet embroidered in clusters of pink and white
plastic flowers, magenta sequins and pearls with silver
metallic thread.
French, circa 1937
Designed by Schiaparelli
Gift of Julia B. Henry, 1978.288.21 bcd

105 HAT

Black wool felt in shape of a shoe.
French, 1937-38
Designed by Schiaparelli
Gift of Rose Messing, 1974.139

106 EVENING GLOVE

Black suede cuffed in blue-green fox.
French, circa 1938
Designed by Alexandre, Paris
Gift of Mrs. G. Macculloch Miller, 1976.37.26a

107 HAT

White milan straw with hatband of black taffeta striped in red
and white.
American, circa 1938
Designed by Norman Norell for Hattie Carnegie
Gift of Mrs. Byron C. Foy, CI 53.40.31

108 HAT

Pink silk trimmed with pale pink clipped willow feathers.
American, 1939
Label: Henri Bendel, New York
Gift of Mrs. Harrison Williams, CI 48.24.2

90 DAY BOOT Belgian early 20th century

1940

109 HAT

Ombre-shaded green silk petals with face veil.
American, 1942
Designed by Germaine Vittu, New York
Gift of Mrs. Alexander P. Morgan, 1972.193

110 EVENING BOLERO

Garnet red velveteen with black fabric appliqués, trimmed
with silver passementerie and jet beads.
(Part of a complete costume).
French, 1946-47
Designed by Balenciaga
Gift of Jean Sinclair Tailer, CI. 64.13.3

111 FAN

Sticks of black lacquered wood mounted with black organdy
petals which form a deep flounce when open.
French, circa 1948
Irene Lewisohn Bequest, 1977.198.2

112 SHOE

Emerald green suede with black leather heel and platform
sole.
American, 1948
Designed by Beleganti
Gift of the Guild of Better Shoe Manufacturers Inc.,
CI 48.12.1b

113 GLOVE

Black kid, rust colored suede, printed with motif of the
handwriting of Alfred de Musset.
American, late 1940s
Label: Mark Cross
Gift of Mary Sykes Crahan, 1973.138.3a

114 HAT

Black faille, small cap and large brim extended at sides with
attached ties which thread through loops on the crown to
raise and lower flaps.
French, 1950s
Designed by Schiaparelli
Gift of Janet Sloane, 1979.87.71

115 HANDBAG

Black suede with brass sticks and guards.
American, circa 1950
Gift of Mrs. Shirley Feinberg, 1980.37.4

116 SHOE

Purple suede trimmed with gold kidskin.
Italian, 1953
Label: Ferragamo's, Florence
Gift of Salvatore Ferragamo, 1973.282.6

117 COCKTAIL HAT

Lemon yellow satin with pompon of matching crushed satin
topped with white silk full-blown rose.
French, 1955
Designed by Balenciaga
Gift of Mrs. Byron C. Foy, CI 56.60.12

118 SHOE

Cream satin and tulle embroidered with silver threads and
rhinestones.
French, 1957
Label: Roger Vivier, Christian Dior
Gift of Valerian Stux-Rybar, 1979.472.23a

119 SHOE

Red leather with red nylon stocking rolled at ankle.
American, 1958-60
Label: Herbert Levine
Gift of Beth Levine, 1976.166.10a

100 GLOVE French late 1920s early 1930.

104 HANDBAG French circa 1937

1960

120 EVENING JACKET

Bolero beaded in red stones, crystals, pearls and silver beads with rhinestones. (Part of a complete costume.)
French, early 1960s
Designed by Givenchy
Gift of Mrs. John Hay Whitney, 1974.184.5b

121 EVENING SHOE

Turquoise satin trimmed all over with transparent peacock blue beads and clear rhinestones.
French, 1960
Label: Roger Vivier, Christian Dior
Gift of Valerian Stux-Rybar, 1979.472.4b

122 SHOE

Purple and green warp-printed silk.
French, 1961
Label: Roger Vivier, Christian Dior
Gift of Valerian Stux-Rybar, 1979.472.18a

123 COCKTAIL HAT

Glossy black raffia band with bright red cotton pompon.
American, 1961
Label: William J.
Gift of Glady Whitfield Solomon, 1977.412.41

124 HAT

Green wire covered with pale silver-green silk leaves and dangling red plastic cherries.
American, circa 1962
Gift of Mrs. Charles Townsend, 1978.79.5

125 EVENING JACKET

Pearl white satin beaded in geometric pattern of pearlescent beige, bronze and gray crystal, Russian sable cuffs.
French, 1962
Designed by Marc Bohan for Christian Dior
Gift of Mrs. Charles B. Wrightsman, CI 64.20.1b

126 HAT

Concentric circles of fine straw in red, white, royal blue and yellow.
American, circa 1963
Designed by Halston
Gift of Mrs. Mortimer Solomon, 1975.301.22

127 PILLBOX HAT

Rose pink velvet.
French, circa 1963
Designed by Balenciaga
Gift of Janet Sloane, 1979.87.34

128 EVENING JACKET

Constructed of pearls of various sizes and shapes in a scrolling leaf pattern.
French, 1965
Designed by Givenchy
Gift of Mrs. Charles B. Wrightsman, CI 66.44.1b

129 HAT

Black varnished paper with looped strip at centre of crown extending down to a point at the side.
American, 1966
Label: Emme
Gift of the Fashion Group, 1975.295.14

130 HELMET HAT

Black velvet bound in black grosgrain with circular cut-out for face.
French, 1967
Designed by Pierre Cardin
Gift of Pierre Cardin, 1977.25.2c

131 EVENING BAG

Gold brushed metal paved with rhinestones.
American, circa 1967
Label: Judith Leiber
Gift of Judith Leiber, 1978.38.1

132 EVENING JUMPSUIT WITH ATTACHED SHOES

Clear vinyl pump with medium clear acrylic heel attached to jumpsuit of leopard print chiffon.
American, 1967
Label: Herbert Levine
Gift of Beth and Herbert Levine, 1977.287.2a

121	EVENING SHOE	French 1966
118	EVENING SHOE	French 1957
96	HANDBAG	French 1925
127	PILLBOX HAT	French circa 1963
105	HAT	French 1937-38
101	HANDBAG	French circa 1934

121

118

96

127

101

105

Select Bibliography

ADBURGHAM, Alison — A view of fashion. London: Allen & Unwin, 1966

BAILLEN, Claude — Chanel solitaire. London: Collins, 1973; New York: Quadrangle/New York Times, 1974

BATTERSBY, Martin — The decorative Thirties. New York: Walker, 1969: London: Studio Vista, 1969

BEATON, Cecil — The glass of fashion. London: Weidenfeld & Nicolson, 1954

BURRIS-MEYER, Elizabeth — This is fashion. New York: Harper, 1943

CALASIBETTA, Charlotte (Editor) — Fairchild's dictionary of fashion. New York: Fairchild, 1975

CARTER, Ernestine — The changing world of fashion. New York: Putman, 1977

CARTER, Ernestine — Magic names of fashion. Englewood Cliffs (N.J.); Prentice-Hall, 1980

CARTER, Ernestine — Twentieth century fashion; a scrapbook, 1900 to today. London; Metheun, 1975

CHASE Edna & Ilka — Always in Vogue. London: Victor Gollance, 1954

CHIERICHETTI, David — Hollywood costume design. London: Studio Vista, 1976

CHARLES-ROUX, Edmonde — Chanel. New York: Knopf, 1975

CORSON, Richard — Fashions in make-up. London: Peter Owen, 1972

DARS, Celestine — A fashion parade: Seeberger collection photographs 1910-50. London: Blond & Briggs, 1979

DE MARLY, Diana — The history of haute couture 1850-1950. London: Batsford. 1980

DE MARLY, Diana — Worth. London: Batsford, 1980

DIOR, Christian — Christian Dior and I, translated from the French by Antonia Fraser. New York: Dutton, 1957

DORNER, Jane — Fashion in the Twenties and Thirties. London: Ian Allan, 1973

'ERTE' — Things I remember. London: Peter Owen, 1975

EWING, Elizabeth — Dress and undress. London: Batsford, 1978

EWING, Elizabeth — History of twentieth century fashion. London: Batesford, 1974

FAIRCHILD, John — The fashionable savages. New York: Doubleday, 1965

FERRAGAMO, Salvatore — Shoemaker of dreams. London: Harrap, 1957

GARLAND, Madge — The changing form of fashion. New York: Praeger, 1970; London: Dent, 1970

GARLAND, Madge — The indecisive decade; the world of fashion and entertainment in the Thirties. London: Macdonald, 1968

GARNER, Philippe — The contemporary decorative arts 1940 to the present day. London: Phaidon, 1980

GARNER, Philippe — Phaidon encyclopedia of decorative arts 1890-1940. London: Phaidon, 1978

GLYNN, Prudence & GINSBURG, Madeleine — In fashion. London: Allen & Unwin, 1978

HAEDRICH, Marcel — Coco Chanel; her life, her secrets. Boston: Little & Brown, 1971; London: Hale, 1972

HOWELL, Georgina — In Vogue; six decades of fashion. London: Allen Lane, 1975

KEENAN, Brigid — The woman we wanted to look like. London: Macmillan, 1977

LAMBERT, Eleanor — World of fashion. New York: Bowker, 1976

LATOUR, Anny — Kings of fashion. New York: Coward McCann, 1958

LAVER, James — Between the wars. London: Vista, 1961

LAVER, James — The concise history of costume. London: Thames & Hudson, 1969

LEE, Sarah Tomerlin — American fashion, edited by S.T. Lee for the Fashion Institute of Technology. New York: Quadrangle/New York Times, 1976

LEVIN, Phyllis — The wheels of fashion. New York: Doubleday, 1965

LYNAM, Ruth — Paris fashions; the great designers and their creations. London: Michael Joseph, 1972

MADSEN, Axel — Living for design. New York: Delacorte, 1979

MARWICK, Arthur — Women at war. London: Fontana, 1977

MUSEE DE LA MODE ET DU COSTUME — Paris 1945-1975; elegance et creation. Paris: Palais Galliera, 1977

OSMA, Guillermo de — Mariano Fortuny; his life and work. New York: Rizzoli, 1980

PACKER — The art of Vogue covers. London: Octopus, 1980

PERCIVAL, John — The World of Diaghilev. rev. ed. London: Herbert Press, 1979

PERKINS, Alice K. — Paris couturiers and milliners. New York: Fairchild, 1949

PICKEN, Mary B. & MILLER, Dora L. — Dressmakers of France. New York: Harper, 1956

POIRET, Paul — King of fashion; the autobiography of Paul Poiret. Philadelphia: Lippincott, 1931

QUANT, Mary — Quant by Quant. New York: Putman, 1966; London: Cassell, 1966

ROCHAS, Marcel — Vingt-cinq ans d'elegance a Paris. Paris: Pierre Tisne, 1951

RUBINSTEIN, Helena — My life for beauty. London: Bodley Head, 1964

SALZ, Barbara & MORRIS, Bernadine — The fashion makers. New York: Random House, 1980

SASSOON, Vidal — Sorry I kept you waiting, Madam. London: Cassell, 1968

SAUNDERS, Edith — The age of Worth. New York: Longmans & Green, 1954

SCHIAPARELLI, Elsa — Shocking life. New York: Dutton, 1954; London: Dent, 1954

THAARUP, Aage — Heads and tales. London: Cassell, 1956

WHITE, Palmer — Paul Poiret. London: Studio Vista, 1973

WILSON, Eunice — A history of shoe fashions. London: Pitman, 1969

Periodical articles

'A biographical sketch', by Jeanne LANVIN, in Vogue (New York), November 15, 1927.

'Philip Mangone', by Philip MANGONE in Vogue (New York), October 1, 1940.

Background Notes

This selection of non-vocal light popular music from 1907 to 1967, is played in a sophisticated style by modern orchestras of the world. It was decided to forsake the use of original records of the period.

As the restricted dynamics of mechanical recordings almost make them an auditory offence for contemporary listening.

'OVERTURE': Jerome Kern sets the background mood for the *haute couture* collection and style of the legendary women of international society.

'LA BELLE EPOQUE': The extravagance and ostentation of society is reflected in the exuberance of the operettas, waltzes and light music of the decade.

'WORLD WAR I': During this turbulent period, it was ironic that the charming instrumental novelty 'Nola' should have managed to make such an impact.

'LE JAZZ HOT': The pure jazz sound from New Orleans was refined and made more acceptable to *the dansant* couples and party-goers, as they participated in the 'rage' dances of the day, such as the Charleston and many others.

'GERSHWIN IN PARIS': George Gershwin was feted by London and Paris society; it was during 1928, whilst in Paris, that he wrote 'American in Paris'.

'THE CLASSIC FRENCH FILMS OF THE 1930s': Rene Clair's first sound film 'Under the Roofs of Paris', 1929, made while that technique was still a novelty, brought music into action.

'MARLENE TO MARILYN FROM MICHEL': These French arrangements play tribute to three great ladies from the cinema, Marlene Dietrich, Ginger Rogers and Marilyn Monroe.

'PARIS MONTAGE': Sums up the mood and sentiment for Paris – written by American composers living in Hollywood!

'CIAO CHARMAINE! – FROM DINO!': Dolores Del Rio was 'Charmaine' in 'What Price Glory?' in 1927. It was made as a silent film by William Fox. Faced with a rival studio producing sound, Fox added a music track 'Charmaine', a waltz melody whenever Miss Del Rio appeared on the screen.

'ENGLAND SWINGS': Reflects the period when fashion became revitalized by the emergence in London of young designers, led by Mary Quant.

'CODA': In music, a passage forming the completion of a piece?

Selected Music

'OVERTURE'		
THE WAY YOU LOOK TONIGHT	COMPOSER: Jerome Kern	1936
Frank Chacksfield and his Orchestra		
'LA BELLE EPOQUE'		
THE MERRY WIDOW Selection	COMPOSER: Franz Lehar	
Andre Kostelanetz and his Orchestra	First Production Vienna	1905
THE GLOW WORM IDYLL	COMPOSER: Paul Lincke	1907
The Vienna Promenade Orchestra conducted by Hans Hagen		
AH: SWEET MYSTERY OF LIFE		
from 'NAUGHTY MARIETTA'	COMPOSER: Victor Herbert	
George Melachrino and his Orchestra	First Production New York	1910
NIGHTS OF GLADNESS	COMPOSER: Charles Ancliffe	1913
Studio Two Concert Orchestra conducted by Reginald Kilbey		
'WORLD WAR I'		
NOLA	COMPOSER: Felix Arndt	1916
Hans Carste and his String Orchestra		

'LE JAZZ HOT'
WHISPERING
Nelson Riddle and his Orchestra

COMPOSER: Vincent Rose 1920

CHICAGO
Paul Whiteman and the New 'AMBASSADOR' Hotel
Orchestra

COMPOSER: Fred Fisher 1922

FASCINATING RHYTHM
Ralph Grierson and Artie Kane (duo-piano)

COMPOSER: George Gershwin 1924

BLUE ROOM
from 'THE GIRL FRIEND'
Jean Wiener (piano)

COMPOSER: Rodgers and Hart
First Production New York 1926

CRAZY RYTHM
Jackie Gleason Orchestra

COMPOSER: Joseph Meyer 1928

'GERSHWIN IN PARIS'
AN AMERICAN IN PARIS (Symphonic Poem)
New York Philharmonic Orchestra conducted by
Michael Tilson Thomas

COMPOSER: George Gershwin 1928

'THE CLASSIC FRENCH FILMS OF THE 1930s'
UNDER THE ROOFS OF PARIS

COMPOSER: Raoul Moretti 1929-1930

UN CARNET DU BAL (The Dance of Life)
Frank Pourcel and his Orchestra

COMPOSER: Maurice Joubert 1937

'MARLENE TO MARILYN FROM MICHEL'
FALLING IN LOVE AGAIN
from 'THE BLUE ANGEL'

COMPOSER: Frederick Hollander 1929

CHEEK TO CHEEK
from 'TOP HAT'

COMPOSER: Irving Berlin 1935

RIVER OF NO RETURN
from film of same name

COMPOSER: Lionel Newman 1954

All three titles played by Michel Le Grand and his
Orchestra

'PARIS MONTAGE'
APRIL IN PARIS

COMPOSER: Vernon Duke 1932

PARIS IN THE SPRING

COMPOSER: Mack Gordon 1935

THE LAST TIME I SAW PARIS

COMPOSER: Jerome Kern 1941

I LOVE PARIS

COMPOSER: Cole Porter 1953

All four titles played by Michel Le Grand and his
Orchestra

'CIAO CHARMAIN! – FROM DINO'
CHARMAINE
Dino Oliveri and his Orchestra

COMPOSER: Ern Rapee 1927

'ENGLAND SWINGS'
ENGLAND SWINGS
ABC Showband conducted by Kevin Hocking

COMPOSER: Roger Miller 1962

'CODA'
YOU ARE BEAUTIFUL
Andre Kostelanetz and his Orchestra

COMPOSER: Rodgers and Hammerstein 1958

Acknowledgements

THE METROPOLITAN MUSEUM OF ART,
NEW YORK
The Costume Institute
Stella Blum   Curator
Elizabeth Lawrence   Master Restorer
Louise Hamer   Mellon Fellow

NATIONAL GALLERY OF VICTORIA
Rowena Clark   Assistant Curator

ART GALLERY OF NEW SOUTH WALES
Jane de Teliga   Assistant Curator

INTERNATIONAL CULTURAL CORPORATION OF
AUSTRALIA LIMITED
James Leslie   Chairman
Norman Baker   Deputy Chairman
Jean Battersby
Franco Belgiorno-Nettis
Graham Burke
Edmund Capon
Ann Lewis
John Lockhart
David Thomas
Robert Edwards   Executive Director

Jennifer Isaacs   Projects Manager
Robin Pratt   Project Assistant

AUSTRALIA COUNCIL
VISUAL ARTS BOARD
DEPARTMENT OF HOME AFFAIRS

CATALOGUE
Design   Paul Leonard
Colour Photography   The Costume Institute,
                           The Metropolitan Museum of Art,
                           Joshua Greene, photographer.
Production   Clemenger Harvie Pty. Ltd.,
                           Melbourne.

EXHIBITION
Concept   Rowena Clark
Design   Robert Brunton
Music   Jeff Dugan by special arrangement
                           with the Australian Broadcasting
                           Commission.
Lighting   Designed by William Akers by
                           courtesy of the Victorian Arts
                           Centre Trust.
Graphics   Paul Leonard
Construction   Peter Hutchison Display Industries
                           Pty. Ltd.
Mannequins   Mei and Picchi Pty. Ltd.

Photographs of designers and fashion plates: Australian
National Gallery, Givenchy, Guillermo de Osma, Mary
Quant, Maurice Worth, Maison Rabanne, Parfums Grès,
Sotheby's Belgravia, London.

International fashion and costume experts brought to
Australia by Qantas Airways Limited.

Photographers of Designers

Page 18   Jean Philippe Worth   Photographer Unknown
Page 28   Mariano Fortuny   Photographer Unknown
Page 32   Paul Poiret   Photographer Unknown
Page 52   Gabrielle Chanel   Photographer
                                  Sir Cecil Beaton
Page 54   Madeleine Vionnet   Photographer
                                  Sir Cecil Beaton
Page 56   Elsa Schiaparelli   Photographer
                                  Sir Cecil Beaton
Page 66   Christian Dior   Photographer
                                  Sir Cecil Beaton
Page 68   Yves Saint Laurent   Photographer
                                  Sir Cecil Beaton
Page 72   Hubert Givenchy   Photographer Unknown
Page 74   Charles James   Photographer
                                  Sir Cecil Beaton
Page 76   Alix Grès   Photographer
                                  Sir Cecil Beaton
Page 78   Cristobal Balenciaga   Photographer
                                  Sir Cecil Beaton
Page 94   Mary Quant   Photographer David Ba
Page 94   Andre Courrèges   Photographer
                                  Sir Cecil Beaton
Page 96   Pierre Cardin   Photographer
                                  Sir Cecil Beaton
Page 96   Paco Rabanne   Photographer
                                  Sir Cecil Beaton